Jan Betts

Knock at the door

Favourite songs and rhymes
old and new
for young and old
to sing, say and enjoy together

Illustrations by Joan Hickson

Ward Lock Educational

ISBN 0 7062 4029 4

First published 1980
Reprinted 1981, 1982

Knock at the Door cassette tape ISBN 0 7062 4047 2
An accompanying cassette tape contains many of the songs and rhymes found in this book.

Warning: Small variations in tape speed from one machine to another are tolerated by the manufacturers and could result in your cassette sounding out of pitch when played together with tuned percussion instruments, e.g. chimebars, glockenspiels, xylophones, piano and also with recorders.

Designed by Geoffrey Wadsley

Text phototypeset in 'Monophoto' Helvetica by
Servis Filmsetting Ltd, Manchester
and printed in Great Britain by
Hollen Street Press Ltd at Slough, Berkshire
for Ward Lock Educational Ltd
47 Marylebone Lane, London W1M 6AX
A Ling Kee Company

contents

order and details of cassette tape

SIDE 1

Knock at the door
Hello, I'm Jan . . .
Oh, we are fine musicians

at home
Diddle, diddle, dumpling, my son John
Twinkle, twinkle, little star
Star light, star bright
To market, to market, to buy a fat pig
See-saw, Margery Daw
Swing me over the water
Dance to your daddy, my bonnie laddie
Tommy, Tommy, Tommy, Tommy
Wind the bobbin up
Follow-my-leader to London town
Charlie Chaplin went to France
There's a brown girl in the ring
I'm Popeye the sailor man
Three sailors went to sea, sea, sea
The clock is on the dresser
I wish, how I wish, that I had a little house
There was a little house
Hush, little baby, don't say a word

animals
Rat-a-tat-tat
Pussycat, Pussycat, where have you been?
I'm a brave, brave mouse
I think mice are rather nice
There was a farmer had a dog
It's funny, my puppy knows just how I feel
I saw a donkey
Trot, trot, trot
Ride a horse, ride a horse
Horsey, Horsey, don't you stop
Half the time they munched the grass

numbers
One, two, three a-lairy
Hickety, pickety, my black hen
One elephant one fine day
All along the backwater
Five little ducks that I once knew
Five little freckled frogs
Today as I went out to play
There were six little frogs

SIDE 2

smaller animals
Incy, Wincy spider
It's funny how beetles
I saw a slippery, slithery snake
Fiddle-dee-dee
I wish I was a little grub
The owl has great big eyes and a pointed nose
The north wind doth blow

days and months
Monday alone
In the Spring the leaves are budding
I like to think that long ago
Good morning, Mister Wind
Snow, snow, snow no more!
Who saw the footprints in the snow?
I hear thunder

me
My grandmother said, 'Now isn't it queer . . .'
I am one year older now than I was last year

people
I'd like to be a barber, and learn to shave and clip
I wish I lived in a caravan
There was a king who had four sons
I'm going to leave Old Texas now
One-eyed Jack, the pirate chief
Captain Patch the pirate had a crew of fifty-three
'Ferry me across the water . . .'
Michael row the boat ashore

travelling
Sea Shell, Sea Shell
'Flying man, flying man up in the sky . . .'
Would you like to ride in my beautiful balloon?
Space-man, space-man
In eighteen hundred and forty-one
There is a painted bus
Daisy, Daisy, Give me your answer do

strange things
Abracadabra, wizzy woo
A witch wears a long tall hat
Hickory, dickory, dare
There was a man lived in the moon
Betty Botter bought some butter
Fuzzy Wuzzy was a bear
Whether the weather be fine, or whether the weather be not
Oh, we are fine musicians

Tuning

foreword

Knock at the Door came about when Jan Betts was working closely with members of the Cambridgeshire Pre-School Playgroups Association on ways of involving children in simple music-making.

With the help of the P.P.A. members, Jan collected together songs and rhymes which had proved to be most popular with various groups of children with whom they were working. Staff at the Cambridgeshire County Resource Centre then became involved, when we agreed to produce a very basic version of *Knock at the Door*. Recognising its value, we followed this up in 1976 with a more substantial book and cassette tape. The print run was quite large for a locally published and locally promoted book, but it was not very long before we realised that the enthusiastic demand by friends and colleagues concerned with musical education of young children in East Anglia would soon clear our stocks.

It was clear that *Knock at the Door* should be available nationally and indeed internationally and we in Cambridgeshire were delighted when Ward Lock Educational decided to publish this enlarged and enlivened version.

We know that Jan believes that from the earliest age possible music-making should be an experience of pure enjoyment. This has been uppermost in her mind during the creation of *Knock at the Door*. The music is simple and the keys are low enough for young voices. It is Jan's hope that children and adults will read, sing, play or listen, as they follow the words, pictures and music together. It is from these important beginnings that music-making should develop naturally.

Jan Betts and Ward Lock Educational have produced a beautiful and fascinating collection of songs and rhymes, old and new. This book will help those adults who wish to communicate a love of music to young children and to answer their 'Knock at the Door'.

Derick Last
Educational Adviser, Cambridgeshire

key to music

★ indicates that any chosen name can be inserted in the rhyme.

(D) means this piece is written in the key of D major.

Em means E minor.

The three basic major cords D, G, A are used to provide a very simple accompaniment in this piece to be played as chords or single notes on your instruments.

 indicates songs and rhymes to be found on cassette tape.

 tells you that this particular note is D, the same as the keychord major. You could play this note on your chime-bars, recorder, piano or guitar, to help you begin the song when not using the tape.

 means that this tune can be played on a descant and tenor recorder (and on a treble if you can play rather high notes).

When there is no [mouse symbol] it is because there are notes in the tune *lower* than middle C that can only be played on a treble recorder.

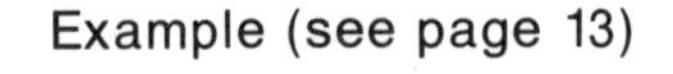

Example (see page 13)

4/4 means that there are 4 beats or 4 strums in each bar throughout the song, and on the tape each song usually has an introduction of 2 bars of these beats e.g:

1 2 3 4 / 1 2 3 4 / Twin - kle, twin - kle, / lit - tle star . . .
D * * * D * * * D * D * G * D * etc.

In this song the chord changes twice in every bar, each chord having 2 beats.

Usually in this book the chords change at the beginning of each bar and on the tape the song keeps the same type of accompaniment as the introductory bars.

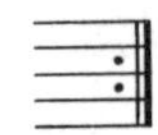 means go back to the beginning and repeat as far as 'Fine'.

guitars and autoharps

There is a tuning section at the end of the tape.

A_7 means this chord can be played simply as an A chord or as an A chord with the decorative 7th added, sounding at its best just before the final keychord in a piece.

This also applies to the other chords with the 7th added.

In this book you will find songs in the keys of C major, D major, G major and A minor, using a minimum of 7 chords or a maximum of 10 chords – shown below.

Dm_7 is used instead of F chord where, in fact, F chord could be played.
Dm_7 is a simpler chord to play (sounds attractive too) and will prepare you for fingering F chord, when you wish to.

How to tune your guitar strings using a piano keyboard.

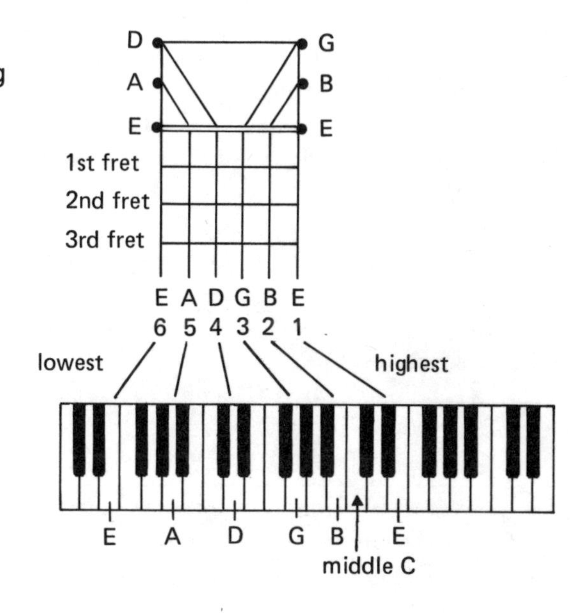

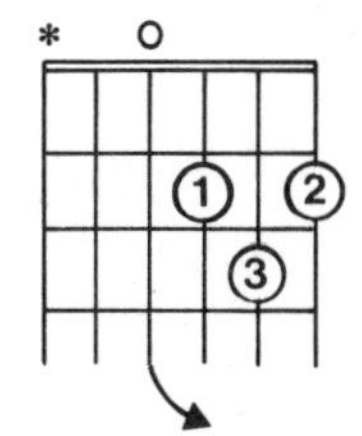

The arrow shows the bass note of the chords and the direction of strums, with the fingers or thumb of the right hand.

* means this string does not fit this chord – 'keep off'.

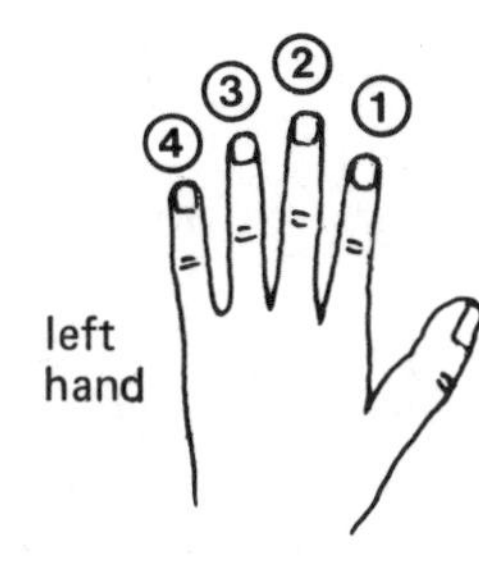

o means this string is played 'open' and not stopped by any left-hand fingers.

①②③ or ④ means this finger of the left hand stops the string behind the fret shown.

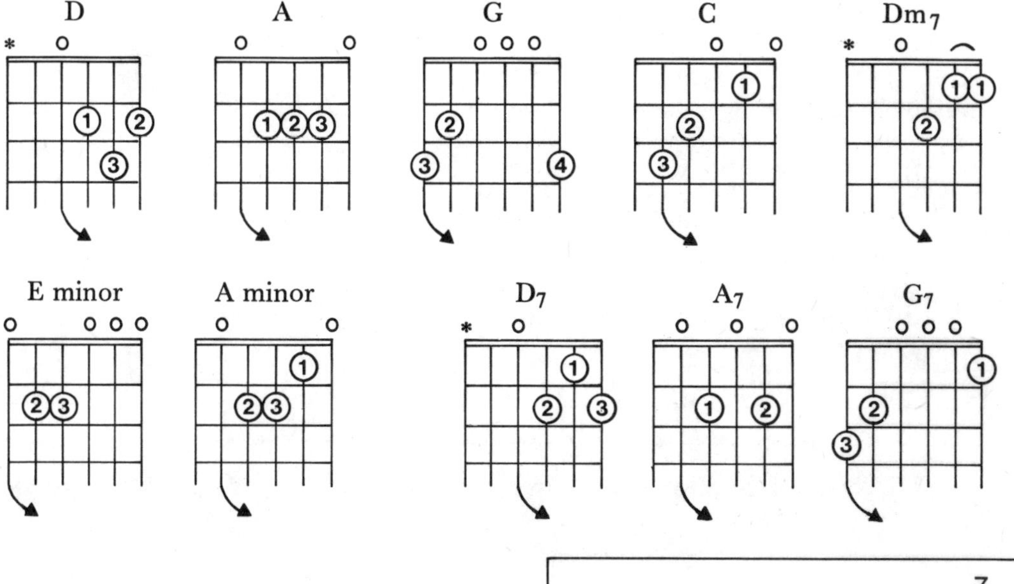

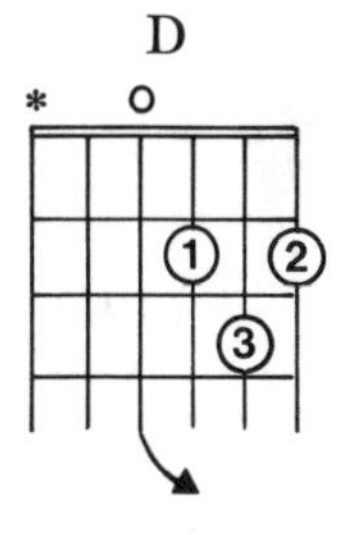

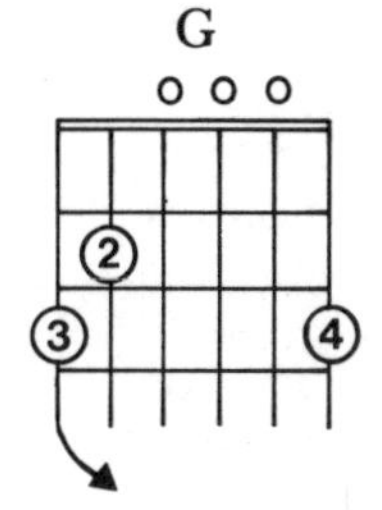

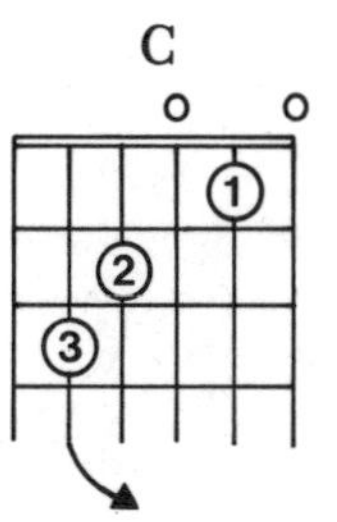

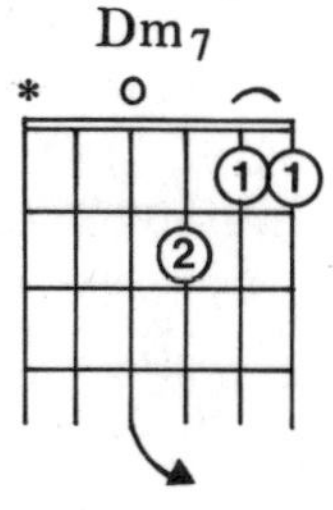

chimebars and how to improvise piano chords

If you have the chimebar notes of the Pentatonic scale only – Middle C D E G A – it is possible to accompany all the songs in this book, playing the single notes marked throughout. (This Pentatonic scale in C is ideal for young children to use and experiment with, giving a pleasing effect when played together in any combination.)

Here are the 5 chimebar notes:

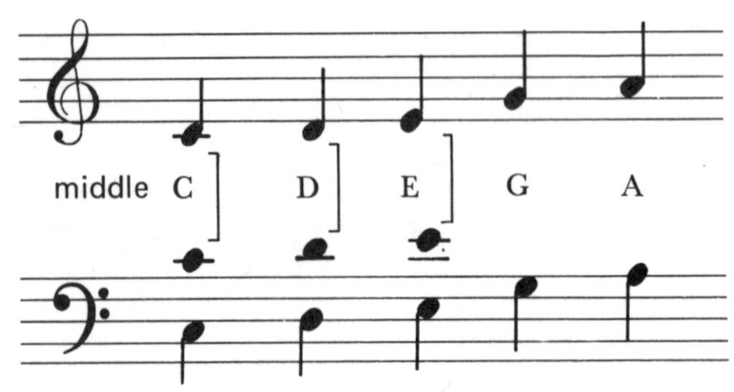

The lower stave shows the same notes written in the bass clef 𝄢: and an octave (or 8 notes) below, which could be played as a simple bass accompaniment on the piano, while you play the melody with your right hand.

If you wish to play more than a single note bass accompaniment with your left hand, a simple 2 or 3 note chord built above or around these 5 bass notes sounds well:

Sometimes the melody will meet the accompanying notes and you will only be able to play one or two notes or you will have to play the bass note an octave lower. Keep the accompanying notes high and light, and let the melody set the mood of the song.

Play these progressions in the 3 keys used, until you know them well. (Sometimes you will only need 2 chords.)

Key of C major

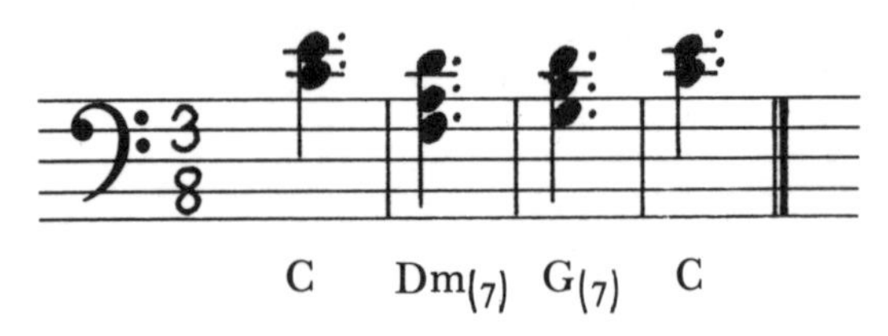

Key of D major (with F♯ and C♯)

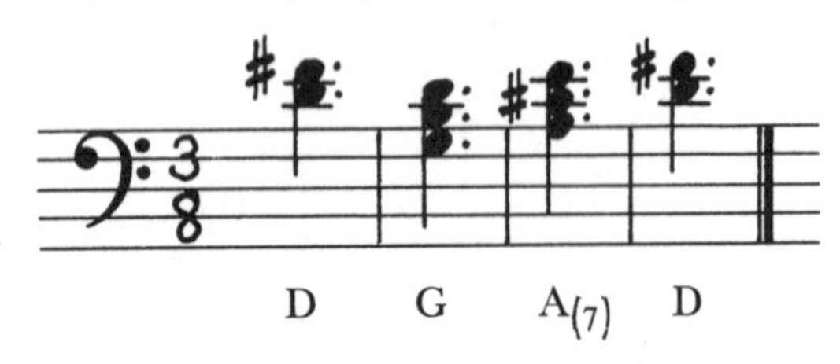

Key of G major (with F♯)

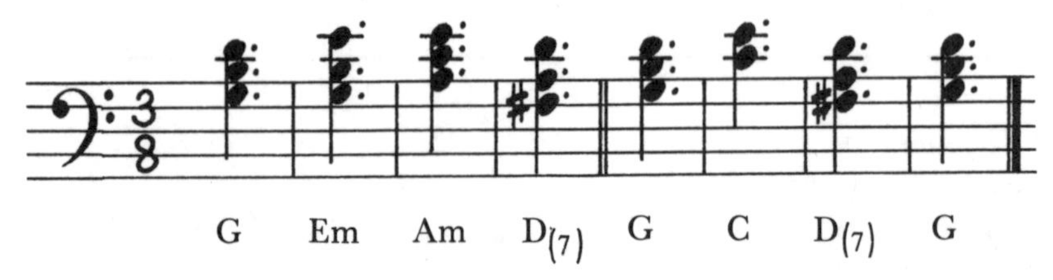

ch. ||: D A :|| In certain songs two notes can be played continually throughout as an 'ostinato' accompaniment. (See pages 37, 62, 74.)

Here are other notes from this Pentatonic scale which can be played with the single notes marked in the song to make a suitable chime-bar accompaniment, perhaps giving an effect of trotting, swaying or just as simple chords:

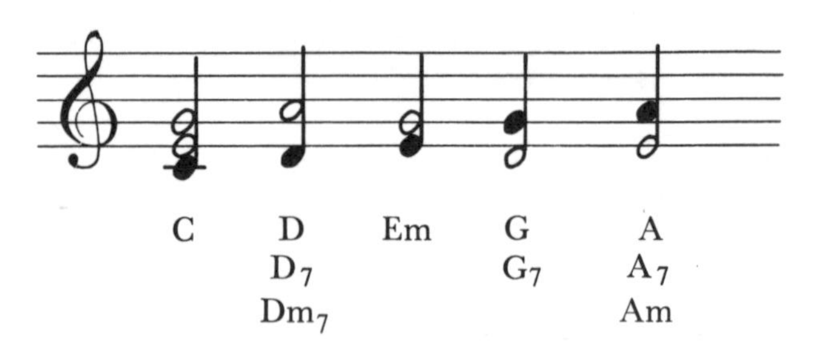

playing a descant recorder

Here are the first 8 notes to learn:

5 more notes:

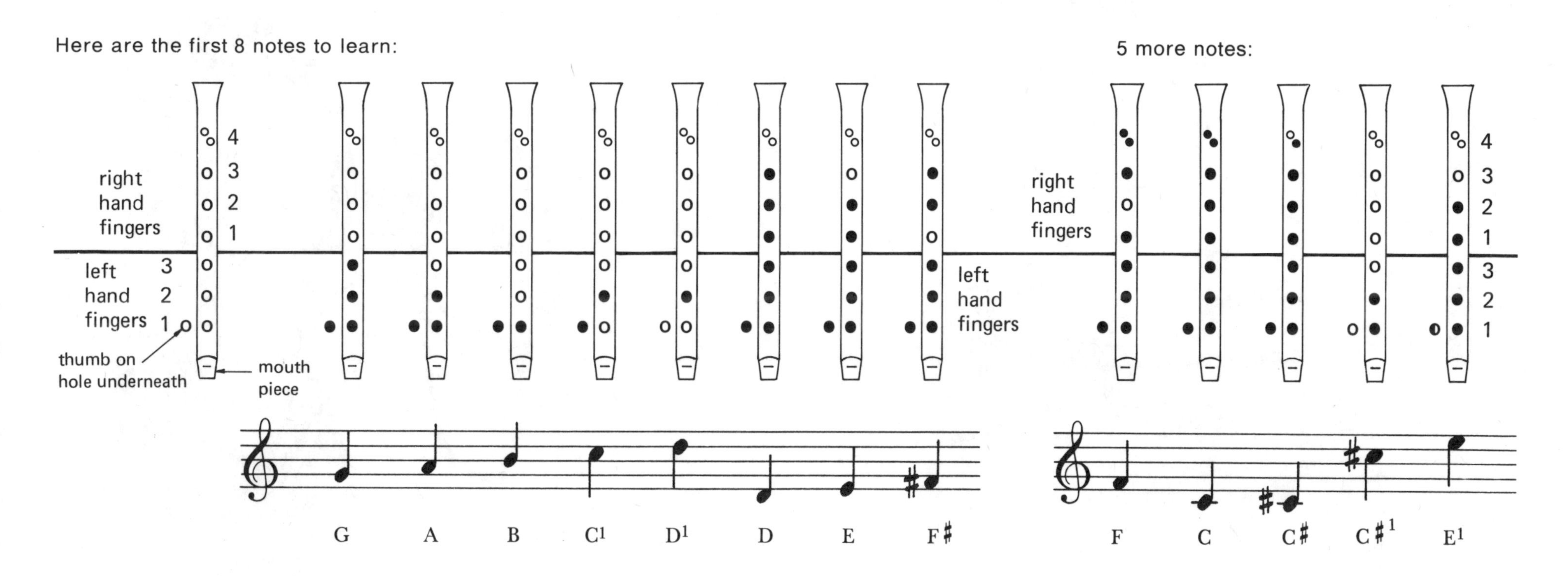

Tunes using only 3, 4, 5 and 6 notes:

Tunes using 6, 7 and 8 notes:

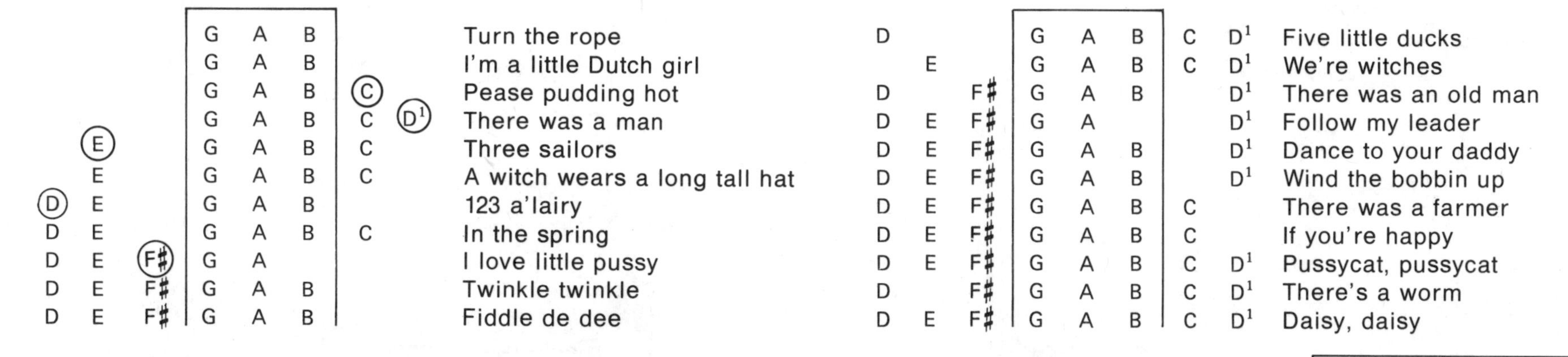

D	E	F♯	G	A	B	C	D^1	Tune
			G	A	B			Turn the rope
			G	A	B			I'm a little Dutch girl
			G	A	B	(C)		Pease pudding hot
			G	A	B	C	(D^1)	There was a man
	(E)		G	A	B	C		Three sailors
	E		G	A	B	C		A witch wears a long tall hat
(D)	E		G	A	B			123 a'lairy
D	E		G	A	B	C		In the spring
D	E	(F♯)	G	A				I love little pussy
D	E	F♯	G	A	B			Twinkle twinkle
D	E	F♯	G	A	B			Fiddle de dee

D	E	F♯	G	A	B	C	D^1	Tune
D			G	A	B	C	D^1	Five little ducks
	E		G	A	B	C	D^1	We're witches
D		F♯	G	A	B		D^1	There was an old man
D	E	F♯	G	A			D^1	Follow my leader
D	E	F♯	G	A	B		D^1	Dance to your daddy
D	E	F♯	G	A	B		D^1	Wind the bobbin up
D	E	F♯	G	A	B	C		There was a farmer
D	E	F♯	G	A	B	C		If you're happy
D	E	F♯	G	A	B	C	D^1	Pussycat, pussycat
D		F♯	G	A	B	C	D^1	There's a worm
D	E	F♯	G	A	B	C	D^1	Daisy, daisy

Knock at the door
Peep in
Lift the latch
Walk in.

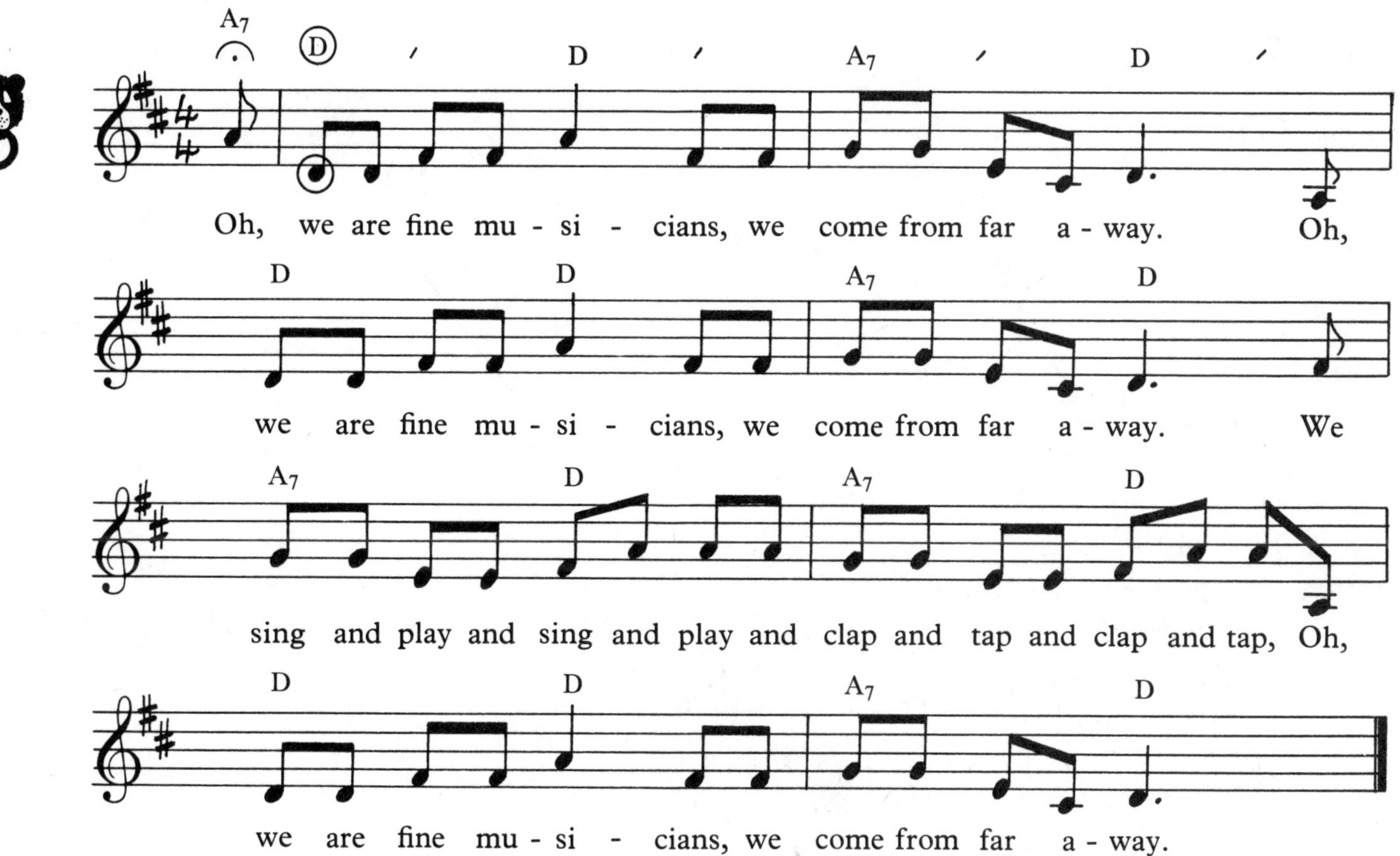
A7
D
D
A7
D
Oh, we are fine mu - si - cians, we come from far a - way. Oh,
D
D
A7
D
we are fine mu - si - cians, we come from far a - way. We
A7
D
A7
D
sing and play and sing and play and clap and tap and clap and tap, Oh,
D
D
A7
D
we are fine mu - si - cians, we come from far a - way.

1· in bed

Diddle, diddle, dumpling, my son John
Went to bed with his trousers on,
One shoe off and one shoe on,
Diddle, diddle, dumpling, my son John.

The man in the moon looked out of the moon,
And this is what he said,
'Tis time that now I'm getting up,
All children are in bed.'

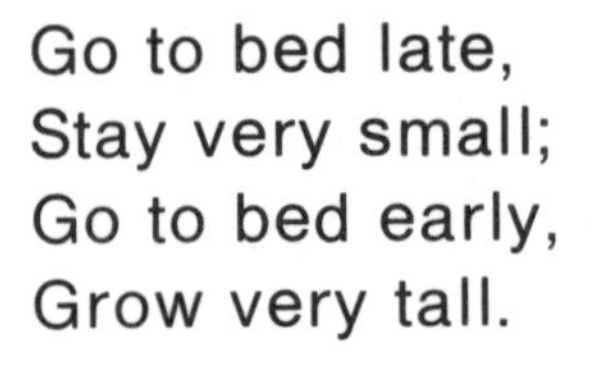

Go to bed late,
Stay very small;
Go to bed early,
Grow very tall.

Go to bed first,
A golden purse,
Go to bed second,
A golden pheasant,
Go to bed third,
A golden bird.

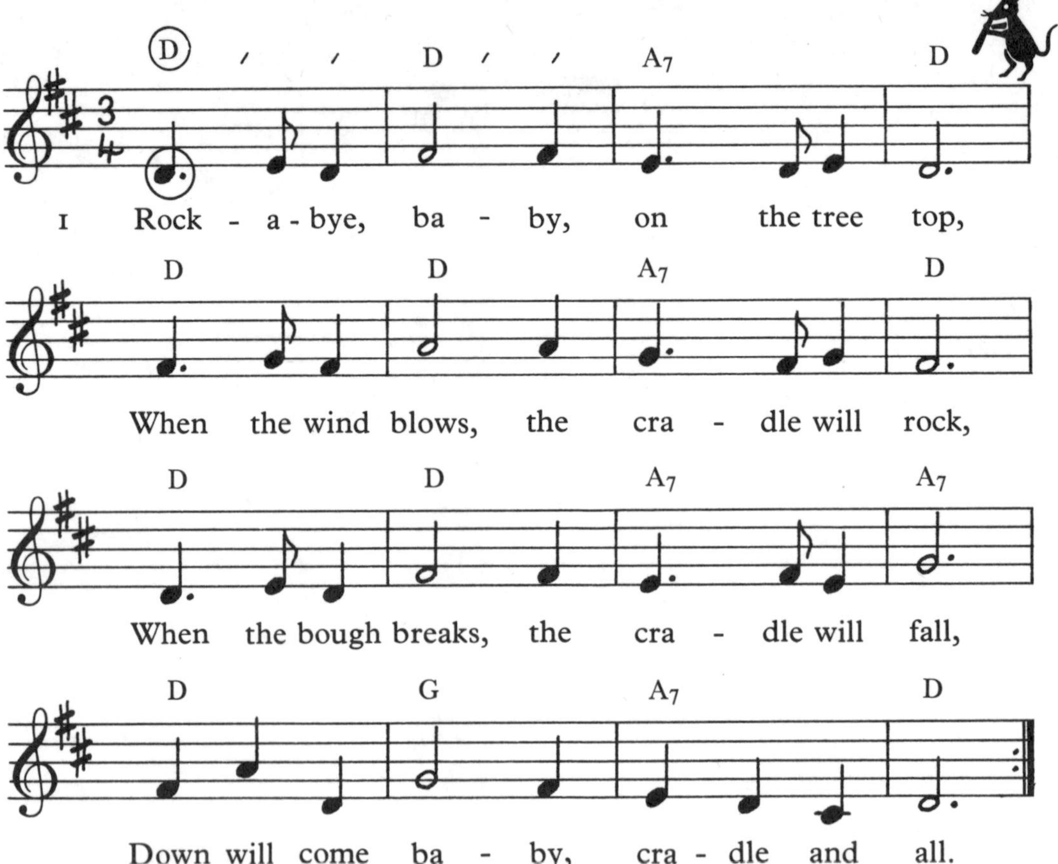

2 Rock-a-bye, baby, thy cradle is green,
Daddy's a nobleman, Mummy's a queen,
Betty's a lady, and wears a gold ring,
Johnny's a drummer, and drums for the king.

There is no need to light a night-light
On a light night like tonight;
For a night-light's light is a slight light
When the moonlight's white and bright.

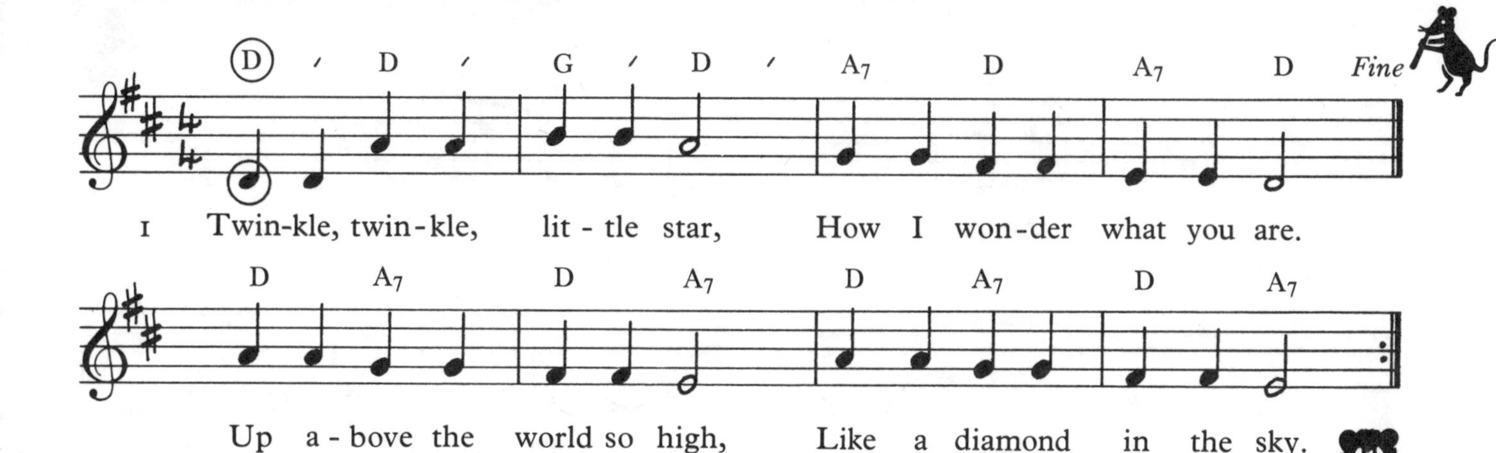

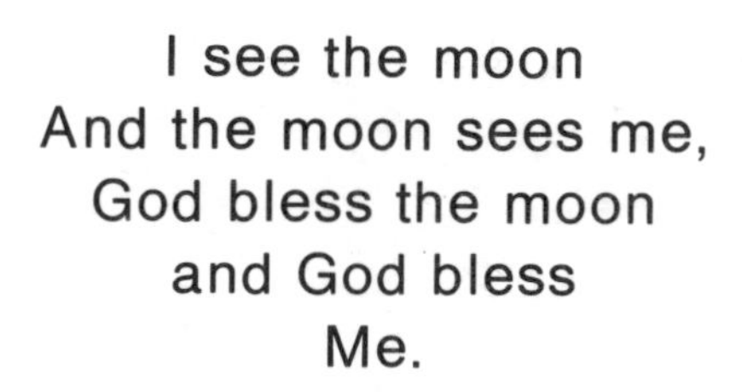

I see the moon
And the moon sees me,
God bless the moon
and God bless
Me.

I see the stars
And the stars see me,
God bless the stars
and God bless
Me.

2 When the blazing sun is gone,
When he nothing shines upon,
Then you show your little light,
Twinkle, twinkle, all the night.

Chorus
Twinkle, twinkle, little star,
How I wonder what you are.

3 Then the traveller in the dark,
Thanks you for your tiny spark,
He could not see which way to go,
If you did not twinkle so.

4 In the dark blue sky you keep,
And often through my curtains peep,
For you never shut your eye,
'Til the sun is in the sky.

Higher than a house,
Higher than a tree;
Oh, whatever can that be?

Star light, star bright,
First star I see tonight,
I wish I may, I wish I might
Have the wish I wish tonight.

Red sky at night,
Shepherd's delight;
Red sky in the morning,
Shepherd's warning.

I saw a star slide down the sky,
Blinding the north as it went by,
Too lovely to be bought or sold,
Too burning and too quick to hold,
Good only to make wishes on
And then forever to be gone.

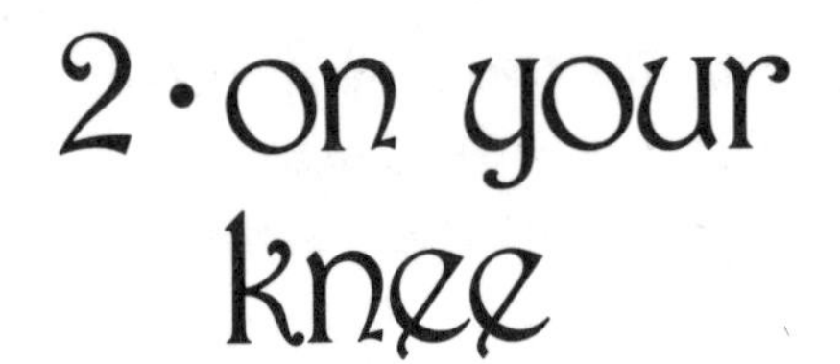

I love coffee,
I love tea,
I love sitting here
On your knee.

2 See-saw, sacradown,
Which is the way to London Town?
One foot up and the other foot down,
That is the way to London Town.

3 See-saw, Jack in the hedge,
Which is the way to London Bridge?
Put on your shoes, and away you trudge,
That is the way to London Bridge.

To market, to market, to buy a fat pig,
Home again, home again, jiggety-jig.
To market, to market, to buy a fat hog,
Home again, home again, jiggety-jog.
To market, to market, to buy a plum bun,
Home again, home again, market is fun.

This little pig went to market,
This little pig stayed at home,
This little pig had roast beef,
This little pig had none,
And this little pig went 'Wee, wee, wee,
I can't find my way home.'

2 Dance to your daddy, my bonnie laddie,
Dance to your daddy, my bonnie lamb.
When you are a mannie you shall work with daddy,
Hold the catch as steady as another man.
Dance to your daddy, my bonnie laddie,
Dance to your daddy, my bonnie lamb.

Bring Daddy home
With a fiddle and a drum,
A pocket full of spices,
An apple and a plum.

Swing me over the water,
Swing me over the sea,
Swing me over the garden wall,
And swing me home for tea.

★

How many days have **we** to play?
Saturday, Sunday, Monday,
Tuesday, Wednesday, Thursday, Friday,
Saturday, Sunday, Monday.

3 · fingers

(Point to each finger of one hand then go backwards.)

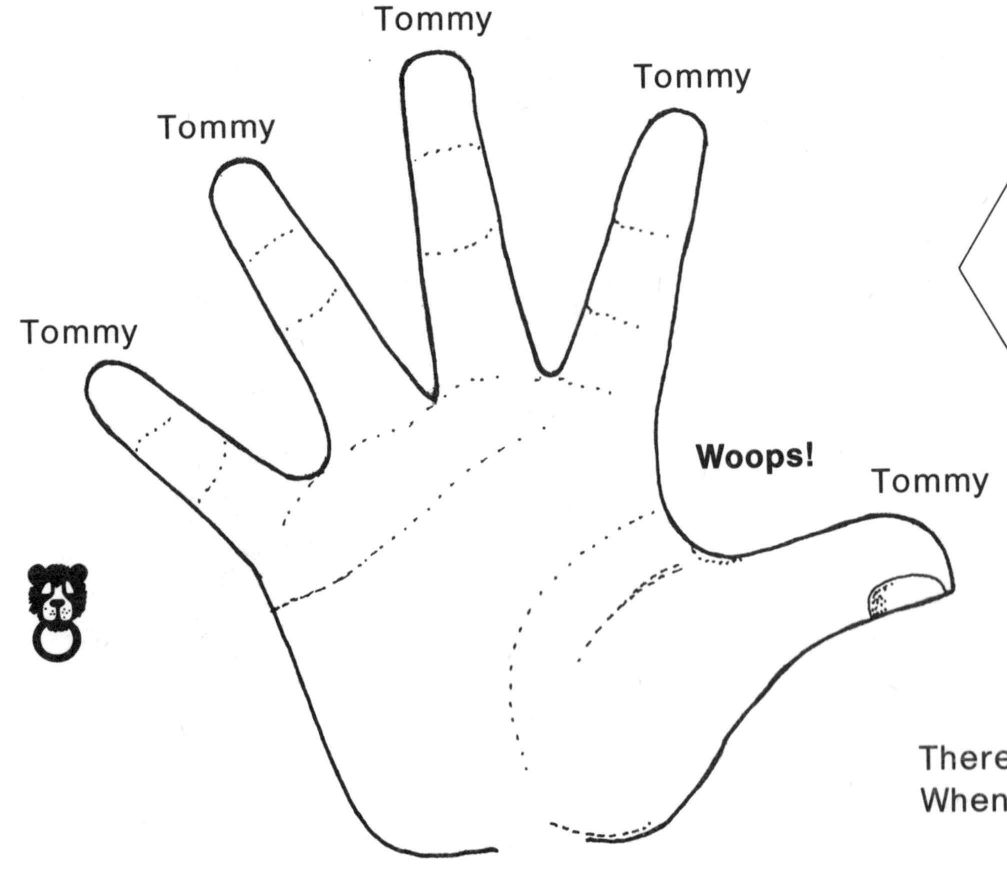

Tommy, Tommy, Tommy, Tommy,
Woops!
Tommy . . . *(thumb)*
Woops!
Tommy, Tommy, Tommy, Tommy.

(Ten fingers doing actions.)
Ten little soldiers standing up straight,
Ten little soldiers open the gate;
Ten little soldiers make a big ring,
Ten little soldiers bow to the king;
Ten little soldiers dancing all day,
Ten little soldiers hiding away.

(Clench hand, put finger through.)
Put your finger in Foxy's hole,
Foxy's not at home.
Foxy's out at the back door
A-picking at a bone.

There was a little mouse, and he lived just there,
When anyone came he ran right up there.

Round and round the garden
Went a teddy bear,
One step,
Two steps,
Jump up in the air!

Round and round the lighthouse,
Up the spiral stair,
One step,
Two steps,
Right up in the air!

Round and round the haystack
Went a little mouse,
One step,
Two steps,
In his little house.

(forefingers)	'Peter Pointer, Peter Pointer, Where are you?' 'Here I am, Here I am, How do you do?'
(middle-fingers)	Toby Tall, Toby Tall, Where are you? . . .
(ring-fingers)	Ruby Ring, Ruby Ring, Where are you? . . .
(little fingers)	Baby Small, Baby Small, Where are you? . . .
(five fingers)	'Fingers all, fingers all, Where are you?' 'Here we are, Here we are, How do you do?'

(thumbs)	Two fat gentlemen met in the lane, Bowed most politely, bowed once again. 'How do you do, how do you do, and How do you do again?'
(forefingers)	Two thin ladies . . .
(middle-fingers)	Two tall policemen . . .
(ring-fingers)	Two young school boys . . .
(little fingers)	Two little babies . . .

My eyes can see,
My ears can hear,
My lips and tongue can talk;
My nose can smell,
My hands can clap,
My feet can run and walk.

10 little fingers,
10 little toes,
2 little eyes and
1 little nose.
2 little cheeks,
1 little chin and
1 little mouth where the toffee goes in!

4 · doing things with fingers

This is my house, *(Fingertips together for roof.)*
This is the door, *(Put tips of index fingers together.)*
The windows are shiny *(Pretend to polish windows.)*
And so is the floor. *(Pretend to polish floors.)*
Outside there is a chimney, *(Hold hands high for the chimney.)*
As tall as can be,
With smoke that goes curling up, *(Wave one hand slowly over the head.)*
Come and see.

I'm going to build a chimney pot
Very, very high.
I'll build it with my bricks
And I'll make it touch the sky.
1, 2, 3, 4, 5, 6, 7, 8, 9, 10 . . .

Build a house up, build it high, *(Clenched fists one on top of the other.)*
Point the chimney to the sky. *(Stretch up a pointing finger.)*
See the roof, *(Make hands into a roof shape.)*
See the floor, *(Make hands into a flat shape.)*
See the little yellow door.
See the mother making bread, *(Make a mixing, kneading action.)*
See the baby going to bed. *(Rest head on folded hands.)*
See the children, all at play,
Dancing through the busy day. *(Make fingers run over lap.)*

Here is a bridge,
Here is a man.
He wants to go over –
Do you think he can?

One step, two steps, three steps, four . . .
He is **nearly** over with –
One step more.

Here is a bridge,
Here is a man.
He wants to go under –
Do you think he can?

One step, two steps, three steps, four . . .
He is **nearly** under with –
One step more.

Here are Grandma's glasses,
Here is Grandma's hat,
This is the way she folds her hands
And puts them in her lap.
(with a deeper voice)
Here are Grandad's glasses,
Here is Grandad's hat,
This is the way he folds his arms
And has a little nap.

Here is the church,
Here is the steeple,
Open the doors, And here are the people.
Here is the parson, going upstairs,
Here he is saying his prayers.

Here are Mummy's knives and forks,
Here is Daddy's table,
Here's my sister's looking-glass,
And here's the baby's cradle.

5 · follow-my-leader

Follow-my-leader, follow-my-leader,
Follow-my-leader after me.
Follow me up to the top of the hill,
And follow me down to the sea.

* *(The leader changes to another action: hand-clapping, slapping knees, stamping feet, shrugging shoulders, etc.)*

You twiddle your thumbs and clap your hands
And then you stamp your feet.
You turn to the left, you turn to the right
You make your fingers meet.
You make a bridge, you make an arch,
You give another clap.
You wave your hands, you fold your hands
Then put them in your lap.

Stretch up high, as tall as a house,
And curl up small, as small as a mouse,
And now pretend you have a drum
And beat like this, rum, tum, tum.
Shake your fingers, stamp your feet,
Close your eyes and go to sleep.

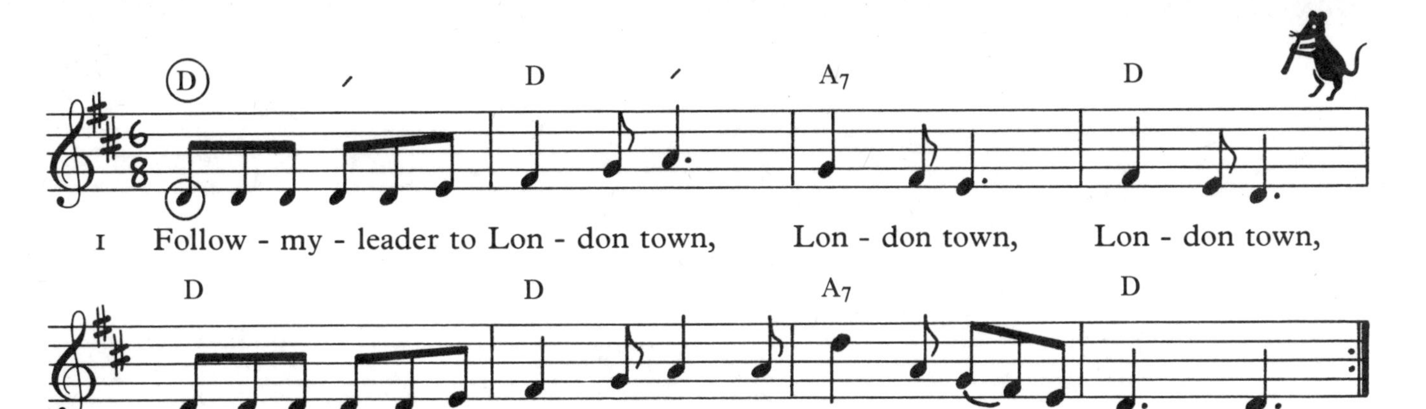

2 Play on your drum to London town, London town . . .

3 Play on your violin to London town, London town . . .

4 Play your recorder to London town, London town . . .

(Go in a crocodile, copying leader.)

1 Hey jim a-long, jim a-long Jos-ie.
Hey jim a-long, jim a-long Jo.

2 Walk jim along . . .

3 Hop jim along . . .

4 Jump jim along . . .

5 Crawl jim along . . .

6 Swing jim along . . .

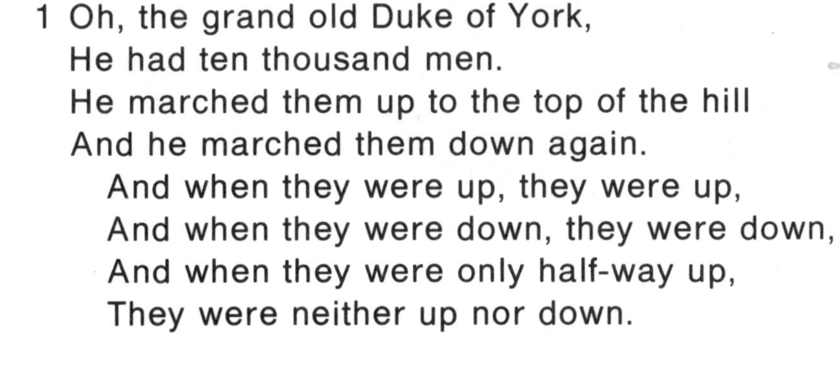

I like to skip,
I like to jump,
I like to run about.
I like to play,
I like to sing,
I like to laugh and shout.

1 Oh, the grand old Duke of York,
He had ten thousand men.
He marched them up to the top of the hill
And he marched them down again.
And when they were up, they were up,
And when they were down, they were down,
And when they were only half-way up,
They were neither up nor down.

2 Oh, the grand old Duke of York,
He had ten thousand men.
They played their drums to the top of the hill,
And they played them down again . . .

3 Oh, the grand old Duke of York,
He had ten thousand men.
They played their pipes to the top of the hill,
And they played them down again . . .

6 · skipping . . .

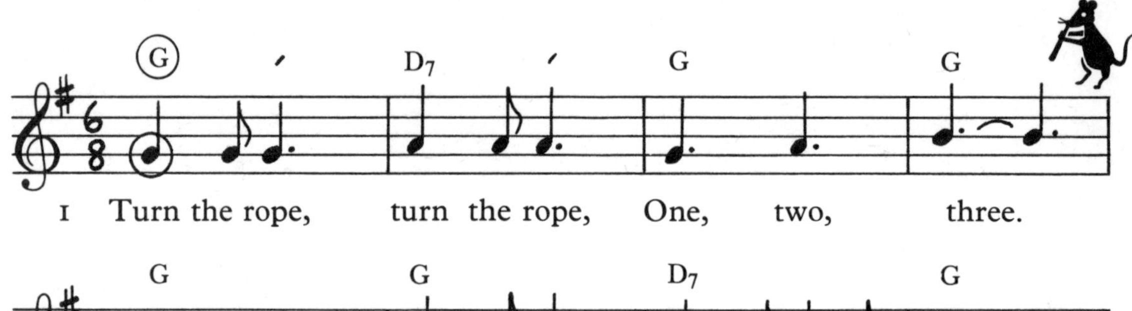

The high skip,
The sly skip,
The skip like a feather,
The long skip,
The strong skip,
Let's all skip together.

The slow skip,
The toe skip,
The skip double-double,
The fast skip,
The last skip,
The skip against trouble.

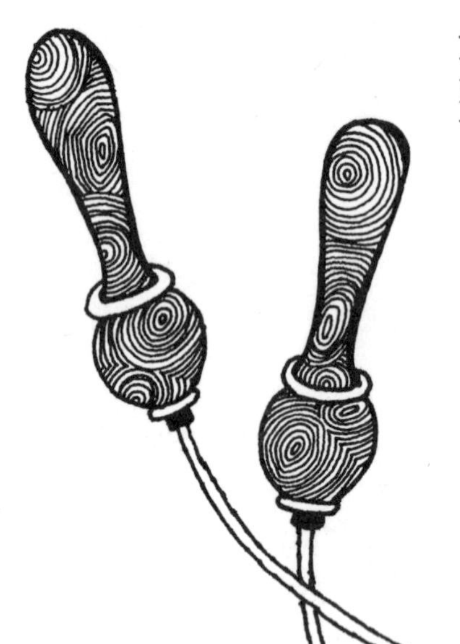

2 Swing the rope,
Swing the rope,
Eight, nine, ten.
Twirl the rope,
Twirl the rope,
Over the rope again.

Wave to Mr Skippy,
If you miss the rope you're out!

Mary Poppins lost her stocking
In, out, on.

Teddy bear, teddy bear, touch the ground,
Teddy bear, teddy bear, turn right round.
Teddy bear, teddy bear, show your shoe,
Teddy bear, teddy bear, that will do.
Teddy bear, teddy bear, run upstairs,
Teddy bear, teddy bear, say your prayers.
Teddy bear, teddy bear, switch off the light,
Teddy bear, teddy bear, say 'Goodnight'.
Salt, mustard, vinegar, pepper . . .
(getting faster and faster)

High, low, skip, dolly, pepper,
High . . . low . . . swing . . . dolly . . . pepper . . .

I like coffee,
I like tea,
I like ★ in with me.

House to let, apply within,
When I go out, ★ comes in.

... around

There's a brown girl in the ring, Tra-la-la-la-la, There's a brown girl in the ring, Tra-la-la-la-la-la,

Brown girl in the ring, Tra-la-la-la-la, for she's sweet like a sugar and a plum, plum, plum.

Go and choose a partner, Tra-la-la-la-la, Go and choose a partner, Tra-la-la-la-la-la,

Go and choose a partner, Tra-la-la-la-la, for she's sweet like a sugar and a plum, plum, plum.

Sally go round the sun
Sally go round the moon
Sally go round the chimney-pots
On a ***Sunday** afternoon – Hey!

**Monday, Tuesday, Wednesday, Thursday, Friday, Saturday*

All in together, girls,
Never mind the weather, girls,
When I call your birthday
Please run out . . .
(January, February, March, April,
May, June, July, August,
September, October, November, December)

Charlie Chaplin went to France
To teach the ladies how to dance.
First he did the rhumba,
Then he did the kicks,
Then he did the samba,
Then he did the splits.

7 · clapping . . .

Tiddly Wink the barber
Went to shave his father;
The razor slipped
And cut his lip,
Tiddly Wink the barber.

2 I'm a little Dutch boy, Dutch boy, Dutch boy . . .
3 Go away, I hate you, hate you, hate you . . .
4 Why do you hate me, hate me, hate me? . . .
5 Because you stole my necklace, necklace, necklace . . .
6 What colour was it, was it, was it? . . .
7 It was gold, gold, gold . . .
8 Here is your necklace, necklace, necklace . . .
9 Now we're getting married, married, married . . .

I saw Esau sawing wood
And Esau saw I saw him.
Though Esau saw I saw him saw,
Still Esau went on sawing.

I had a little bumper car,
Number forty-eight,
I went round the corner
And forgot to pull the brakes.

I'm Popeye the sailor man.
Full stop! (*clap clap*)
I live in a caravan. Full stop!
I opened the door,
Fell flat on the floor,
I'm Popeye the sailor man.
Full stop! Full stop! Full stop!

Tinker, tailor, soldier, sailor,
Rich man, poor man, begger man, thief.

Silk, satin, cotton, rags . . .

Coach, carriage, wheelbarrow, dustcart . . .

This year, next year, sometime, never . . .

... and dipping

Dip, dip, dip,
My blue ship,
Sailing on the water
Like a cup and saucer.
Dip, dip, dip,
You're not 'it'!

Each, peach, pear, plum,
I spy Tom Thumb.
Tom Thumb in the wood,
I spy Robin Hood.
Robin Hood in the cellar,
I spy Cinderella.
Cinderella at the ball,
I spy Henry Hall.
Henry Hall in his house,
I spy Mickey Mouse.
Mickey Mouse with his mum,
Each, peach, pear, plum.

Ip, skip, sky blue,
Who's it? Not you.
Not because you're dirty,
Not because you're clean,
Not because your mother
Says you're the fairy queen.
O - U - T spells out
So out you must 'go'!

Ibble, obble, black bobble,
Ibble, obble, out.
Turn a little dishcloth inside out.

If it's not dirty, turn it back again,
Ibble, obble, black bobble,
Ibble, obble, out.

Mickey Mouse bought a house
What colour was it? (*choose colour*)
'Blue'
B - L - U - E spells blue
And you must have it on '**you**'!

Mickey Mouse bought a house
What number was it? (*choose number*)
'Seven'
1 - 2 - 3 - 4 - 5 - 6 - 7
And you are not **'it'**!

8 · in the house

The clock is on the dresser,
  Tick, tick, tock.
The baby's in the cradle,
  Rock, rock, rock.
The rain is on the window,
  Pitter, pitter, pat.
The sun is coming out –
  So we'll clap, clap, clap!

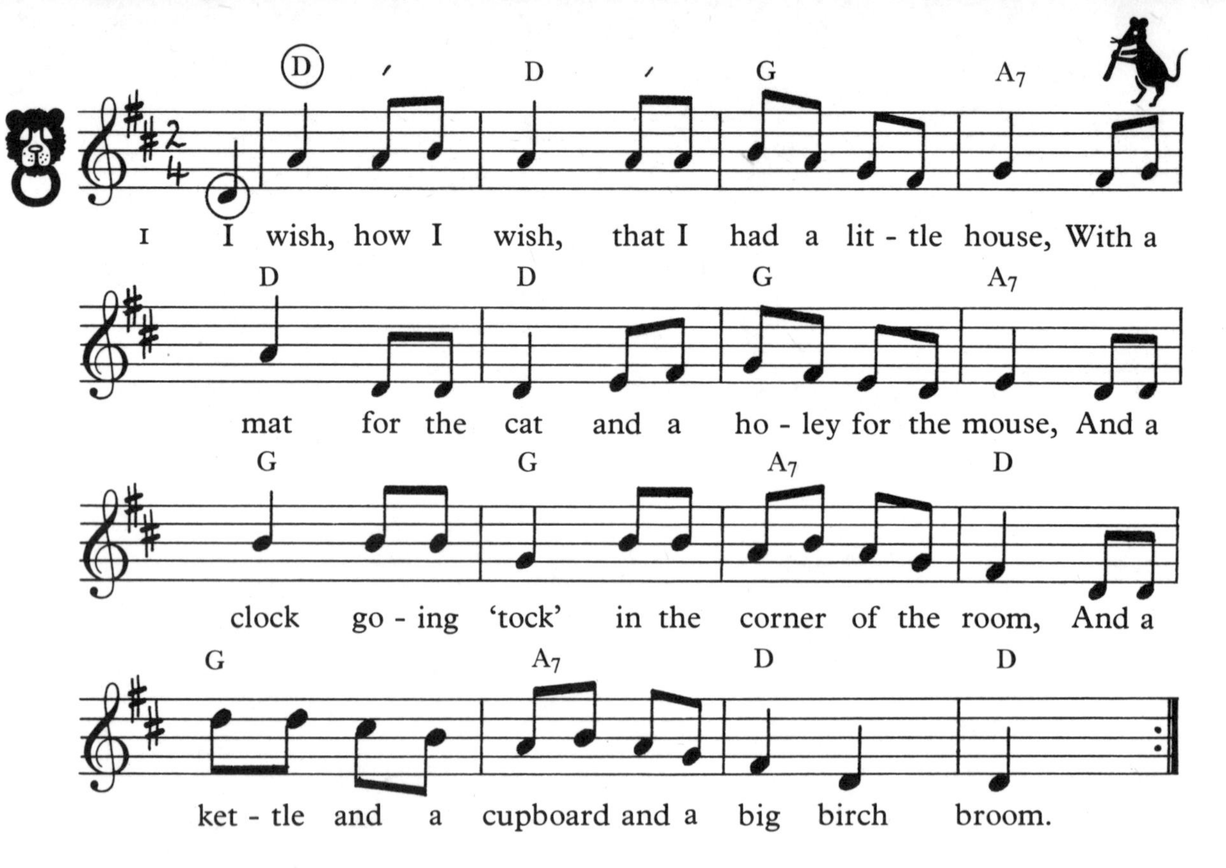

2 To school in the morning the children off would run,
 And I'd give them a kiss and a penny for a bun,
 But directly they had gone from this little house of mine,
 I'd clap my hands and snatch a cloth, and shine, shine, shine.

3 I'd shine all the knives, all the windows, all the floors,
 All the grates, all the plates, all the handles on the doors,
 Every fork, every spoon, every lid and every tin,
 Till everything was shining like a bright new pin.

4 At night, by the fire, when the children were in bed,
 I'd sit, and I'd knit, with a cap upon my head,
 And the kettles and the saucepans they would shine, shine, shine,
 In this teeny little, cosy little house of mine.

I went into a street one day.
  What was in the street?
A house.
  What was in the house?
A kitchen.
  What was in the kitchen?
A cupboard.
  What was in the cupboard?
A box.
  What was in the box?
BISCUITS – YUM, YUM!! (*loudly*)

(Make other stories in this way.)

village	country
lane	fields
cottage	farm
room	barn
table	kennel
drawer	dog
work-box	WOOF, WOOF!!
scissors	
SNIP, SNAP!!	

This is the key of the kingdom:
In that kingdom there is a city.
In that city there is a town.
In that town there is a street.
In that street there is a lane.
In that lane there is a yard.
In that yard there is a house.
In that house there is a room.
In that room there is a bed.
On that bed there is a basket.
In that basket there are some flowers.
  Flowers in a basket,
  Basket on the bed,
  Bed in the room,
  Room in the house,
  House in the yard,
  Yard in the lane,
  Lane in the street,
  Street in the town,
  Town in the city,
  City in the kingdom.
Of the kingdom this is the key.

9 · tea-time

Cross-patch,
Draw the latch,
Sit by the fire and spin;
Take a cup, and drink it up,
Then call your neighbours in.

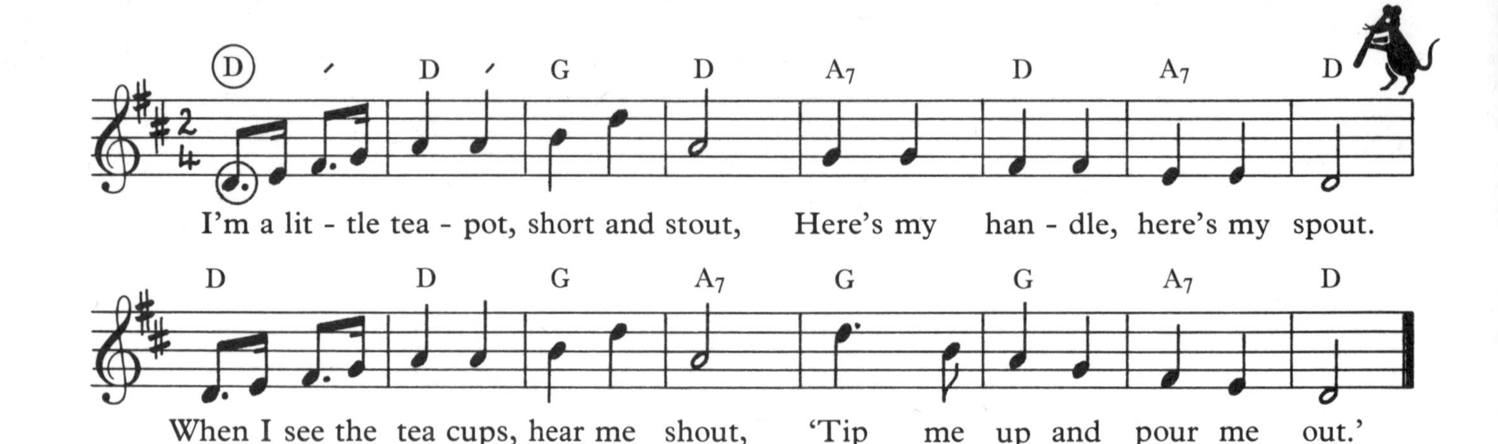

(Do actions making body into pot with handle and spout.)

There was a little house,
And it had a little door,
And I knocked on the knocker –
1 - 2 - 3 - 4.
Out came a little lady
And curtsied low to me –
And said 'Will you come inside, Sir,
And have a cup of tea?'

(Do actions with hands.)

This is my saucer,
This is my cup,
And this is the way
I lift it up!

This is my saucer,
This is my cup,
Pour in the milk
And drink it up.

Bubble, said the kettle,
Bubble, said the pot,
Bubble, bubble, bubble,
We are very, very hot.

Shall I take you off the fire?
No, you need not trouble.
That is just the way we talk
Bubble, bubble, bubble.

One, two, three –
Mummy caught a flea.
Put it in the teapot to make a cup of tea.
The flea jumped out,
Mummy gave a shout,
In came Daddy with his shirt hanging out!

Pease pudding hot, Pease pudding cold, Pease pudding in the pot, Nine days old.
Some like it hot, Some like it cold, Some like it in the pot, Nine days old.

Mix a pancake, stir a pancake,
Pop it in the pan,
Fry a pancake, toss a pancake,
Catch it if you can.

Handy, Spandy, Jack-a-dandy,
Loves plum cake and sugar candy,
He bought some at the grocer's shop
And out he came, hop, hop, hop!

Pat-a-cake, pat-a-cake, baker's man,
Bake me a cake, as fast as you can.
Pat it and prick it and mark it with 'B'
And put in the oven for baby and me.

Porridge is bubbling
Bubbling hot,
Stir it round
And round in the pot.
The bubbles plip,
The bubbles plop,
It's ready to eat,
All bubbling hot.

Little Tommy Tucker
Sings for his supper.
What shall we give him?
White bread and butter.
How shall he cut it
Without a knife?
How shall he marry
Without a wife?

Dibbity, dibbity, dibbity, doe,
Give me a pancake
And I'll go.

Dibbity, dibbity, dibbity, ditter,
Please to give me
A bit of fritter.

10 · buying

There was a big bear
Who lived in a cave;
His greatest love
Was honey.
He had twopence a week
Which he never could save,
So he never had
Any money.
I bought him a money-box
Red and round,
In which to put
His money.
He saved and saved
Till he got a pound,
Then spent it all
On honey.

2 If that diamond ring is brass,
Daddy's going to buy you a looking-glass.
If that looking-glass gets broke,
Daddy's going to buy you a billy goat.

3 If that billy goat won't pull,
Daddy's going to buy you a cart and bull.
If that cart and bull turn over,
Daddy's going to buy you a dog called Rover.

4 If that dog called Rover won't bark,
Daddy's going to buy you a horse and cart,
If that horse and cart fall down,
You'll still be the sweetest little baby in town.

If only I had plenty of money,
I'd buy you some flowers, and I'd buy you some honey,
I'd buy you a boat, and I'd buy you a sail,
I'd buy you a cat with a long bushy tail,
I'd buy you a brooch and a bangle as well,
I'd buy you a church, and I'd buy you the bell,
I'd buy you the earth, I'd buy you the moon –
Oh, money, dear money, please come very soon!

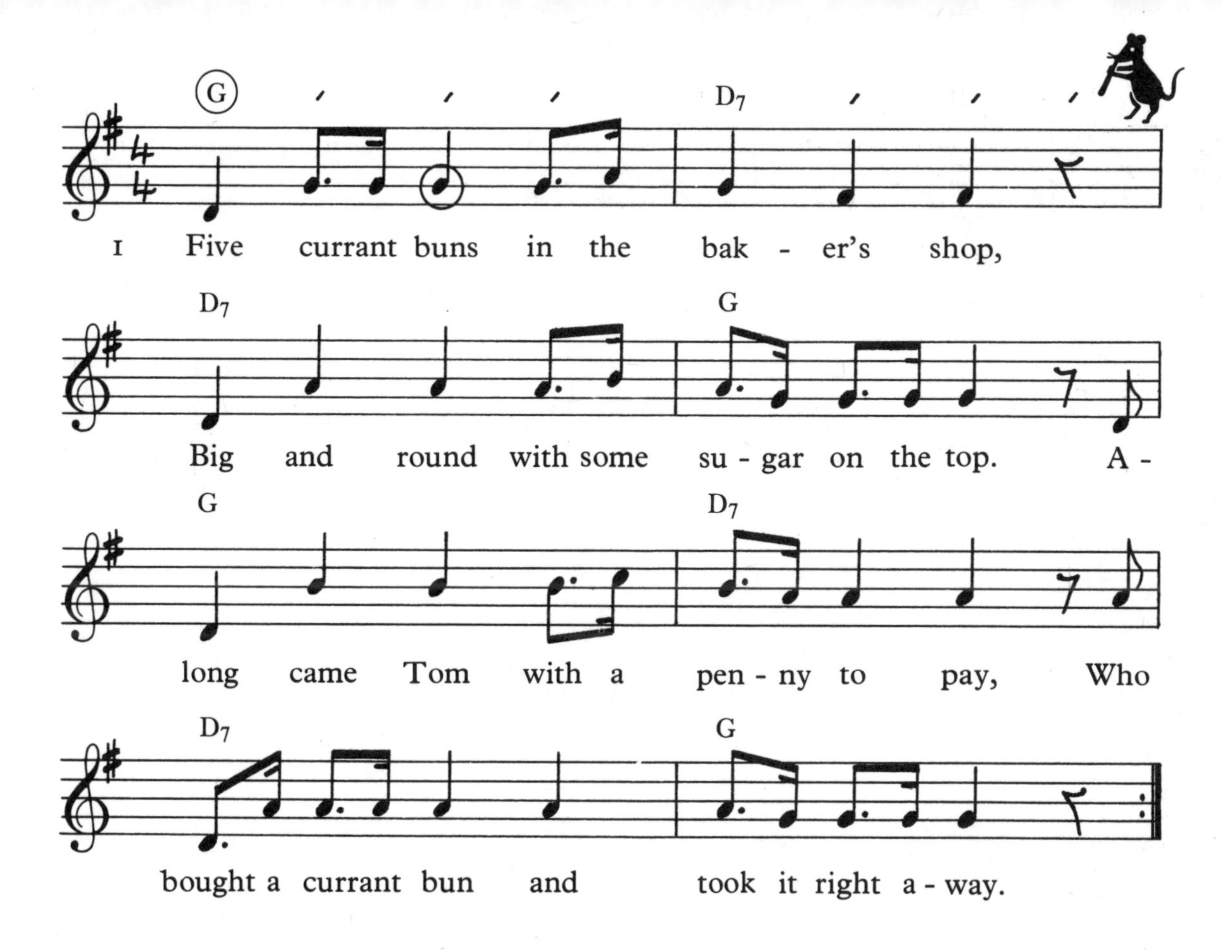

2 Four currant buns in the baker's shop . . .

3 Three currant buns in the baker's shop . . .

4 Two currant buns in the baker's shop . . .

5 One currant bun in the baker's shop . . .

6 No currant buns in the baker's shop,
Big and round with some sugar on the top.
No one came with a penny to pay,
So close the baker's shop and have a baking day.

Sing a song of mincemeat,
Currants, raisins, spice,
Apples, sugar, nutmeg,
Everything that's nice.

Stir it with a ladle,
Wish a lovely wish,
Drop it in the middle
Of your well-filled dish.

Stir again for good luck,
Pack it all away,
Tied in little jars and pots,
Until Christmas Day.

As I was going down Mincing Lane
Mincing Lane on a Christmas Day,
'Hot mince pies!' a pieman cries,
'Two for a penny, and look at the size!'

Christmas is coming, the geese are getting fat,
Please put a penny in the old man's hat.
If you haven't got a penny, a ha'penny will do,
If you haven't got a ha'penny,
God Bless You.

11 · cats

2 So I'll not pull her tail, nor drive her away,
But pussy and I very gently will play.

3 I'll sit by the fire and I'll give her some food,
And pussy will love me because I am good.

Rat-a-tat-tat,
Who is that?
Only Grandma's pussycat.
What do you want?
A pint of milk.
Where's your money?
In my pocket.
Where's your pocket?
I forgot it.
Oh, you silly pussycat!

Diddlety, diddlety, dumpty,
The cat ran up the plum tree;
Half a crown
To fetch her down,
Diddlety, diddlety, dumpty.

Who's that ringing at my door bell?
A little pussycat who isn't very well.
Rub its little nose with a little mutton fat,
And that's the best cure for a little pussycat.

Where are you going,
My little kittens?
We are going to town
To get us some mittens.
What! Mittens for kittens!
Do kittens wear mittens?
Who ever saw little kittens with mittens?

Where are you going,
My little cat?
I'm going to town
To get me a hat!
What! A hat for a cat!
A cat with a hat!
Who ever saw a cat with a hat?

Cats sleep
Anywhere,
Any table,
Any chair,
Top of piano,
Window-ledge,
In the middle,
On the edge,
Open drawer,
Empty shoe,
Anybody's
Lap will do,
Fitted in a
Cardboard box,
In the cupboard
With your frocks –
Anywhere!
They don't care!
Cats sleep
Anywhere.

As I was going to St Ives
I met a man with seven wives,
Every wife had seven sacks,
Every sack had seven cats,
Every cat had seven kittens;
Kittens, cats, sacks, wives –
How many were going to St Ives?

I know a little pussy,
Her coat is silver grey;
She lives down in the meadow
Not very far away.
Although she is a pussy,
She'll never be a cat,
For she's a pussy willow –
Now what do you think of that?

12 · mice

One mouse, two mice,
Three mice, four,
Stealing from their tunnel,
Creeping through the door.

Softly! softly!
Don't make a sound –
Don't let your little feet
Patter on the ground.

There on the hearth-rug,
Sleek and fat,
Soundly sleeping,
Lies old Tom Cat.

If he should hear you,
There'd be no more
Of one mouse, two mice,
Three mice, four.

So please be careful
How far you roam,
For if you should wake him –
He'd – chase – you – all – HOME!

1 What about a cat?
What – a cat?
Yes, a cat!
Big and fat.
Well, except for a cat – I'm not afraid of anything!

2 What about a trap?
What – a trap?
Yes, a trap!
That goes snap.
Well, except for a trap – I'm not afraid of anything!

3 What about an owl?
What – an owl?
Yes, an owl!
On the prowl.
Well, except for an owl – I'm not afraid of anything!

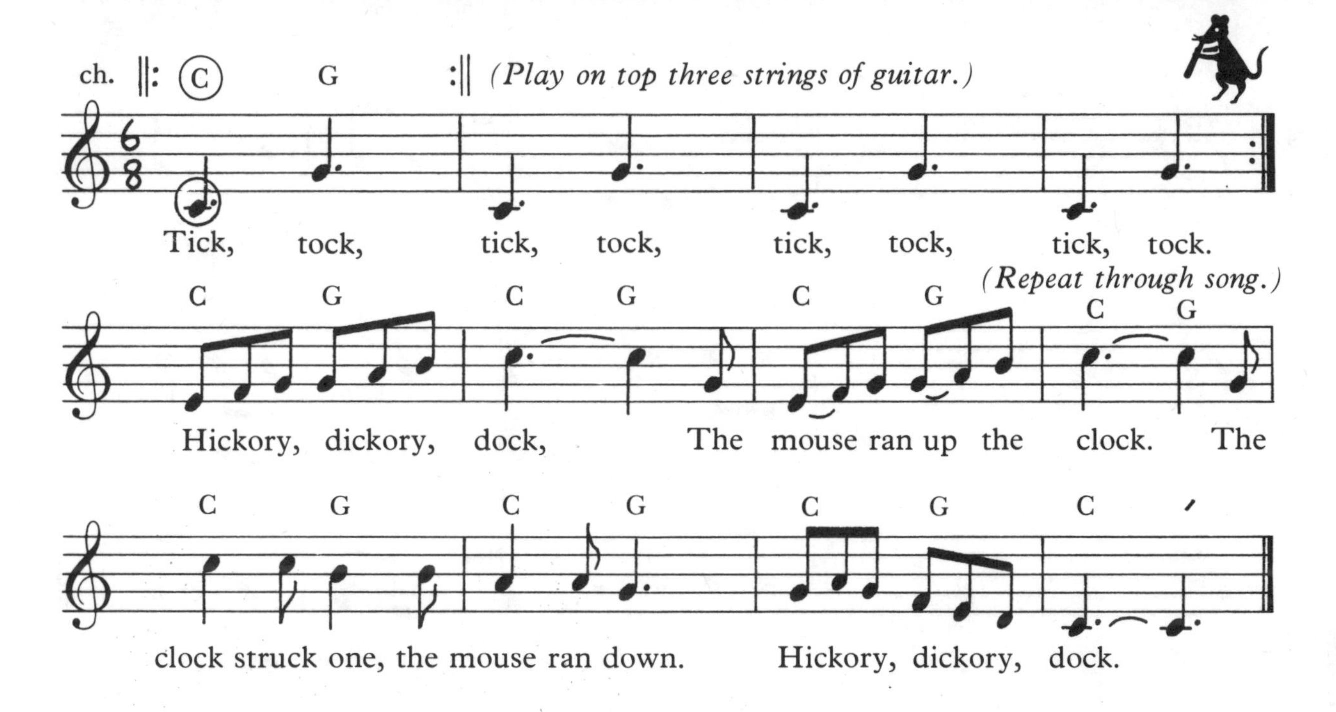

I think mice
Are rather nice.
Their tails are long,
Their faces small,
They haven't any
Chins at all.
Their ears are pink,
Their teeth are white,
They run about
The house at night.
They nibble things
They shouldn't touch,
And no one seems
To like them much.
But I think mice
Are nice.

I know a house, and a cold old house,
A cold old house by the sea,
If I were a mouse in that cold old house,
What a cold old mouse I'd be.

What shall I call
My dear little dormouse?
His eyes are small,
But his tail is e-nor-mouse.

I sometimes call him Terrible John,
'Cos his tail goes on –
And on –
And on.
And I sometimes call him Terrible Jack,
'Cos his tail goes on to the end of his back.
And I sometimes call him Terrible James,
'Cos he says he likes me calling him names –
But I think I shall call him Jim,
'Cos I **am** fond of him.

I see a little mouse,
But he doesn't see me;
If he could see me
How frightened he would be.
Off he would flee
To his little wee house,
Then there'd only be me
And there wouldn't be mouse!

13 · dogs...

G C D7 G

B - i - n - g - o, B - i - n - g - o,

Em Am D7 G

B - i - n - g - o, And Bin-go was his name, Sir.

It's funny,
my puppy
knows just how I feel.

When I'm happy
he's yappy
and squirms like an eel.

When I'm grumpy
he's slumpy
and stays at my heel.

It's funny,
my puppy
knows such a great deal.

There was a young maiden called Maggie
Whose dog was enormous and shaggy;
The front end of him
Looked ferocious and grim –
But the tail end was friendly and waggy.

Old Dog lay in the summer sun,
Much too lazy to rise and run.
He flapped an ear
At a buzzing fly;
He winked a half-opened
Sleepy eye;
He scratched himself
On an itching spot,
As he dozed on the porch
When the sun was hot;
He whimpered a bit
From force of habit,
While he lazily dreamed
Of chasing a rabbit.
But Old Dog happily lay in the sun,
Much too lazy to rise and run.

2 I drive my little donkey, Gee-up, Gee-up,
I drive my little donkey, In a painted cart, In a painted cart.

3 The bells they jingle gaily, Ding-ding, Ding-ding,
The bells they jingle gaily, As off we trot, As off we trot.

If I had a donkey
That wouldn't go
D'you think I'd wallop him?
No! No! No!
I'd put him in a stable
And keep him nice and warm,
The best little donkey
That ever was born.

...and donkeys

I saw a donkey
One day old,
His head was too big
For his neck to hold;
His legs were shaky
And long and loose,
They rocked and staggered
And weren't much use.

He tried to gambol
And frisk a bit,
But he wasn't quite sure
Of the trick of it.
His queer little coat
Was soft and grey,
And curled at his neck
In a lovely way.

His face was wistful
And left no doubt
That he felt life needed
Some thinking about.
So he blundered round
In venturesome quest,
And then lay flat
On the ground to rest.

He looked so little
And weak and slim,
I prayed the world
Might be good to him.

14 · horses

Ride a horse, ride a horse,
Ride a horse to town.
Ride a horse, ride a horse,
Woops! — Fall down!

2 Whoa, whoa, whoa, We've not far to go.
Take me safe my little pony,
Though the way is rough and stony,
Whoa, whoa, whoa, whoa, whoa, We've not far to go.

3 Stay, stay, stay, Time to end our play.
You've brought me safe my little pony,
Though the way was rough and stony,
Stay, stay, stay, stay, stay, Time to end our play.

One to make ready
And two to prepare,
Good luck to the rider
And away goes the mare.

Bell horses, bell horses,
What time of day?
One o'clock, two o'clock,
Three and away.

Hob, shoe, hob,
Hob, shoe, hob,
Here a nail
And there a nail
And that's well shod.

This is the way the ladies ride,
Trit, trit, tree, trit, trit, tree, trit, trit, tree!
This is the way the gentlemen ride,
Gallop-a-trot, gallop-a-trot, gallop-a-trot!
This is the way the farmer rides,
Hobbledy-hoy, hobbledy-hoy, and down into the ditch!

2 Horsey, Horsey, on your way, We've done the journey many a day,
Your tail goes swish and the wheels go round, Giddy up, we're homeward bound.

Ten galloping horses came to town,
Five were white, five were brown;
They galloped up, they galloped down,
And then they galloped right out of town.

Ride a cock-horse to Banbury Cross,
To see a fine lady on a white horse,
Rings on her fingers and bells on her toes,
She shall have music wherever she goes.

Ride a cock-horse to Banbury Cross,
To see what Tommy can buy,
A penny white loaf, a penny white cake
And a two-penny apple pie!

15 · COWS

Half the time they munched the grass, and all the time they lay
Down in the water-meadows, the lazy month of May.
  A-chewing,
  A-mooing,
To pass the hours away.

'Nice weather,' said the brown cow. 'Ah,' said the white.
'Grass is very tasty.' 'Grass is all right.'

Half the time they munched the grass, and all the time they lay
Down in the water-meadows, the lazy month of May.
  A-chewing,
  A-mooing,
To pass the hours away.

'Rain coming,' said the brown cow. 'Ah,' said the white.
'Flies is very tiresome.' 'Flies bite.'

Half the time they munched the grass, and all the time they lay
Down in the water-meadows, the lazy month of May,
  A-chewing,
  A-mooing,
To pass the hours away.

'Time to go,' said the brown cow. 'Ah,' said the white.
'Nice chat.' 'Very pleasant.'
'Night.' 'Night.'

Half the time they munched the grass, and all the time they lay
Down in the water-meadows, the lazy month of May.
  A-chewing,
  A-mooing,
To pass the hours away.

There was an Old Man who said, 'How
Shall I flee from this horrible cow?
I will sit on this stile,
And continue to smile,
Which may soften the heart of that cow.'

Four stiff-standers
Four dilly-danders,
Two lookers, two crookers,
And a wig-wag.

The friendly cow all red and white,
I love with all my heart;
She gives me cream with all her might,
To eat with apple tart.

She wanders lowing here and there,
And yet she cannot stray,
All in the pleasant open air,
The pleasant light of day.

And blown by all the winds that pass
And wet with all the showers,
She walks among the meadow grass
And eats the meadow flowers.

16 · counting

D D G A7

1 This old man, he played one, He played nick-nack on my drum. With a

D D A7 D

Nick-nack, paddy whack, give a dog a bone; This old man came rolling home.

2 This old man, he played two, He played nick-nack on my shoe . . .
3 This old man, he played three, He played nick-nack on my knee . . .
4 This old man, he played four, He played nick-nack on my door . . .
5 This old man, he played five, He played nick-nack on my hive . . .

1, 2, 3, 4,
Mary at the cottage door,
5, 6, 7, 8,
Eating cherries off a plate.

2, 4, 6, 8,
Mary at the garden gate,
Eating cherries off a plate,
2, 4, 6, 8.

wh— wh— wh— wh
One o'clock, two o'clock, three o'clock, four –
I found a fairy clock close to my door.

wh— wh— wh— wh
Five o'clock, six o'clock, seven o'clock, eight –
I blew and I blew, and I found it was late.

wh— wh—
I blew and I blew till I counted to ten –
And now I'm beginning all over again!
wh— wh— WH!

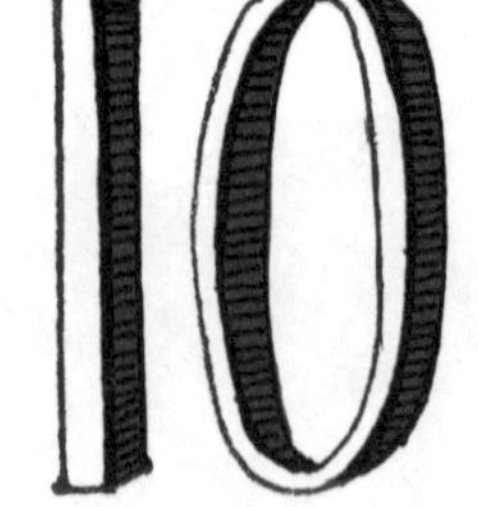

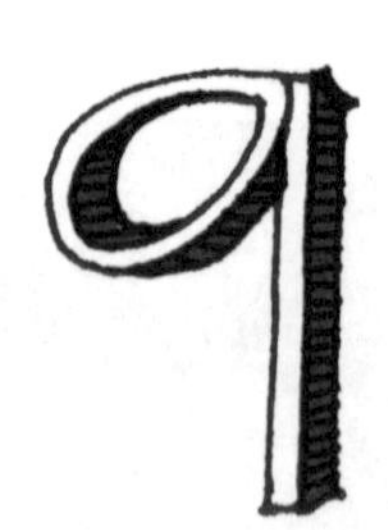

(Five fingers curled up in the other hand.)

Five little peas in a pea pod pressed,
One grew and two grew, and so did all the rest.
They grew and grew and grew and grew
And grew and never stopped, *(open fingers out)*
They grew so plump and portly that the pea pod –
POPPED! *(clap hands together)*

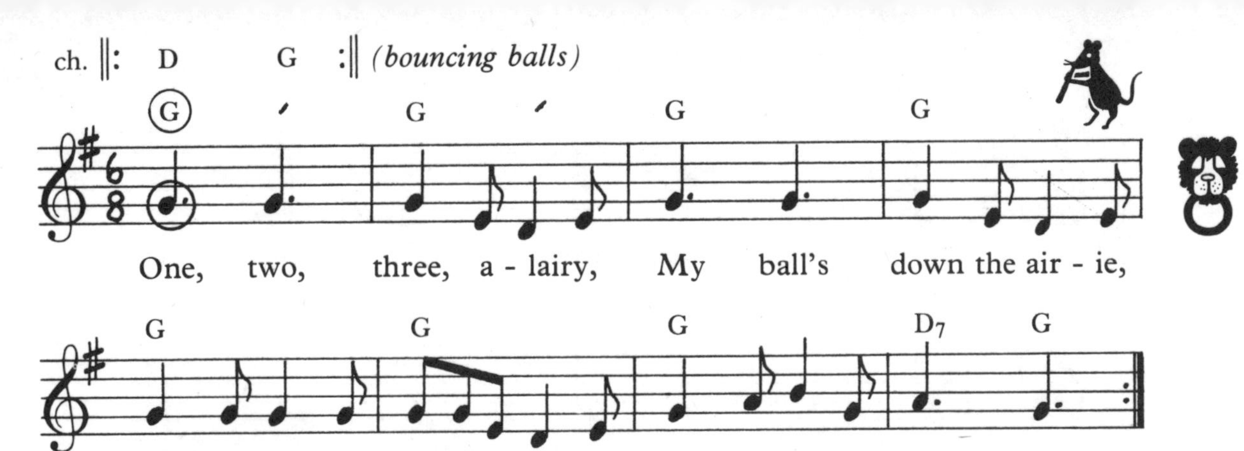

(dipping)

1 potato, 2 potatoes, 3 potatoes, 4,
5 potatoes, 6 potatoes, 7 potatoes more.

Five minutes, five minutes more, please!
  Let me stay five minutes more!
Can't I just finish the castle
  I'm building here on the floor?
Can't I just finish the story
  I'm reading here in my book?
Can't I just finish this bead-chain –
  It almost is finished, look!
Can't I just finish this game, please?
  When a game's once begun
It's a pity never to find out
  Whether you've lost or won.
Can't I just stay five minutes?
  Well, can't I stay just four?
Three minutes, then? two minutes?
  Can't I stay one minute more?

5

4

1, 2, 3, 4, 5,
Once I caught a fish alive,
6, 7, 8, 9, 10,
Then I let him go again.
'Why did you let him go?'
'Because he bit my finger so.'
'Which finger did he bite?'
'This little finger on the right.'

3 2

Big shirts and little shirts
  hanging on the line,
Three shirts of Daddy's,
  three shirts of mine,
Three shirts of Peter's
  and that makes nine.

1

One, two,
Buckle my shoe;
Three, four,
Knock at the door;
Five, six,
Pick up sticks;
Seven, eight,
Lay them straight;
Nine, ten,
A big fat hen;
Eleven, twelve,
Dig and delve;
Thirteen, fourteen,
Maids a-courting;
Fifteen, sixteen,
Maids in the kitchen;
Seventeen, eighteen,
Maids in waiting;
Nineteen, twenty,
My plate's empty.

17 · and adding

Hickety, pickety, my black hen,
She lays eggs for gentlemen;
Sometimes nine, sometimes ten,
Hickety, pickety, my black hen.

2 'Baa, baa, white sheep,
Have you any wool?'
'No, Sir, no, Sir, no bags full.
None to mend the blankets,
None to mend the frocks,
None to mend the little boys
with holes in their socks!'

There were two wrens upon a tree,
Whistle and I'll come to thee;
Another came, and there were three,
Whistle and I'll come to thee;
Another came and there were four,
You needn't whistle any more,
For being frightened, off they flew,
And there are none to show to you.

One little brown bird, up and up he flew,
Along came another one and that made two.

Two little brown birds sitting on a tree,
Along came another one and that made three.

Three little brown birds, then up came one more;
What's all the noise about? That made four.

Four little brown birds, all alive, alive,
Along came another one and that made five.

Five little brown birds sitting on the sticks,
Along came another one and that made six.

Six little brown birds flying up to heaven,
Along came another one and that made seven.

Seven little brown birds sitting on a gate,
Along came another one and that made eight.

Eight little brown birds sat on Mummy's line,
Along came another one and that made nine.

Nine little brown birds saw a lot of men,
So home they flew to Daddy, and that made ten.

Two little cats sitting by the door,
Two more joined them, and then there were four.
Four little cats up to their tricks,
Two more joined them, then there were six.
Six little cats climbing on the gate,
Two more joined them, then there were eight.

18 · with elephants

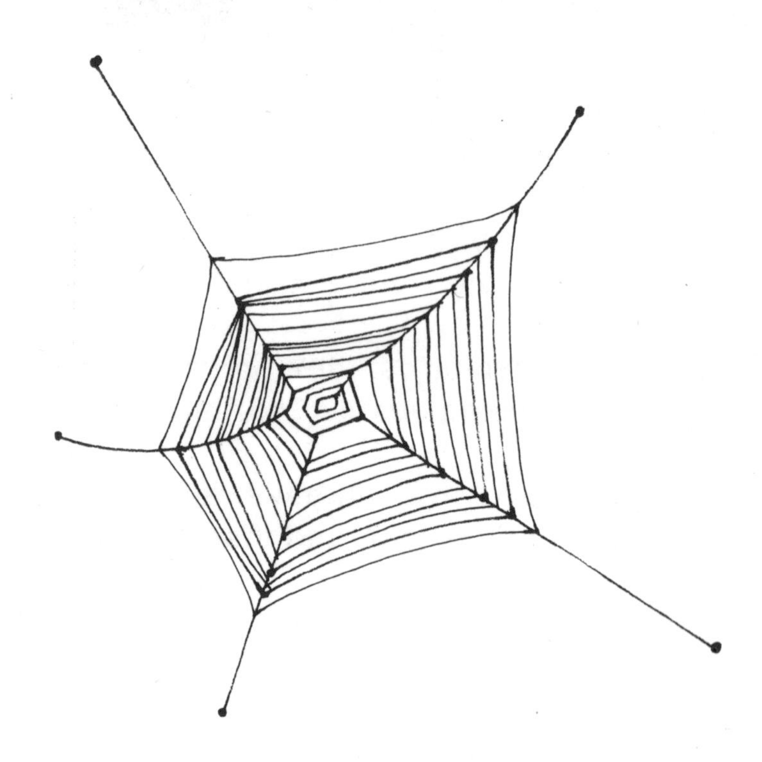

2 Two elephants one fine day,
Went on a spider's web to play,
They found it such tremendous fun,
They called to another elephant to come.

3 Three elephants one fine day,
Went on a spider's web to play,
They found it such tremendous fun,
They called to another elephant to come.

4 Four elephants one fine day,
Went on a spider's web to play,
They found it such tremendous fun,
They called to another elephant to come.

5 Five elephants one fine day,
Went on a spider's web to play,
They found it such tremendous fun,
They stayed and they played all day in the sun.

An elephant goes like this and that,
He's terribly big.
And he's terribly fat.
He has no fingers
And he has no toes,
But goodness gracious,
What a big nose!

The elephant is big and strong,
His ears are large, his trunk is long,
He walks around with heavy tread,
His keeper walking at his head.

When people call this beast to mind
They marvel more and more
At such a little tail behind
So **large** a trunk before.

19 · disappearing ducks

Ducky Daddles
Loves the puddles.
How he waddles
As he paddles
In the puddles –
Ducky-Daddles!

2 Down to the river they would go,
Wibble, wobble, wibble, wobble, to and fro.
But the one little duck with a feather on his back,
He led the others with a quack, quack, quack.
Quack, quack, quack, quack, quack, quack,
He led the others with a quack, quack, quack.

3 Home from the river they would come,
Wibble, wobble, wibble, wobble, ho-hum-hum!
But the one little duck with a feather on his back
He led the others with a quack, quack, quack.
Quack, quack, quack, quack, quack, quack,
He led the others with a quack, quack, quack.

Five little ducks went swimming one day,
Over the pond and far away.
Mother Duck said, 'Quack, quack, quack, quack,'
But only four little ducks came back.

Four little ducks went swimming one day . . .

Three little ducks went swimming one day . . .

Two little ducks went swimming one day . . .

One little duck went swimming one day,
Over the pond and far away.
Mother Duck said, 'Quack, quack, quack, quack,'
And five little ducks came swimming back.

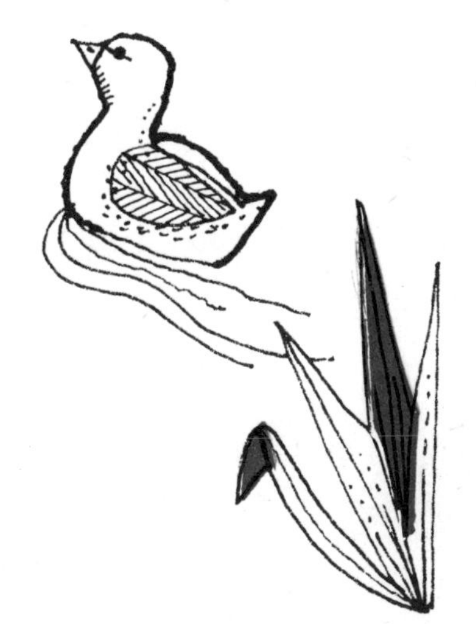

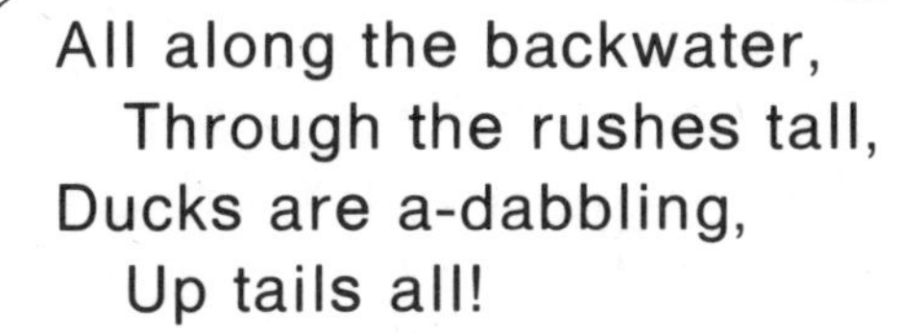

All along the backwater,
  Through the rushes tall,
Ducks are a-dabbling,
  Up tails all!

Ducks' tails, drakes' tails,
  Yellow feet a-quiver,
Yellow bills all out of sight
  Busy in the river!

Slushy green undergrowth
  Where the roach swim,
Here we keep our larder
  Cool and full and dim!

Every one for what he likes!
  We like to be
Heads down, tails up,
  Dabbling free!

High in the blue above,
  Swifts whirl and call –
We are down a-dabbling,
  Up tails all!

20 · and frogs

Underneath the water-weeds
  Small and black, I wriggle,
And life is most surprising!
  Wiggle! waggle! wiggle!
There's every now and then a most
  Exciting change in me,
I wonder, wiggle! waggle!
  What I shall turn out to be!

2 Four little freckled frogs sat on a speckled log . . .

3 Three little freckled frogs sat on a speckled log . . .

4 Two little freckled frogs sat on a speckled log . . .

5 One little freckled frog sat on a speckled log,
Catching some most delicious bugs. Yum, yum.
He jumped into the pool, where it was nice and cool,
Then there were no green freckled frogs — Ahhhh!

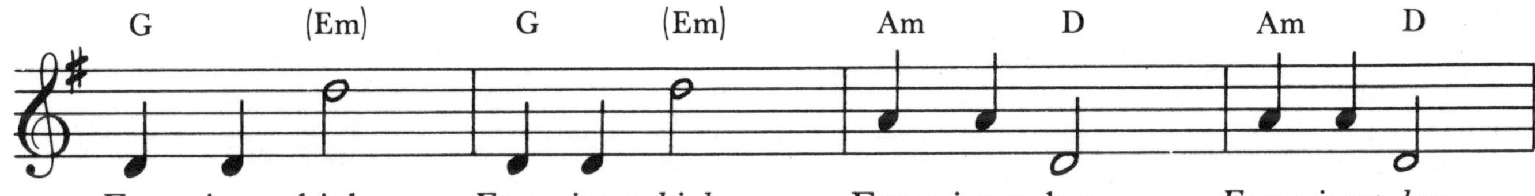

2 Four little frogs
Sitting on a well,
Two leaned over
And down they fell.

Frogs jump high,
Frogs jump low,
Two little frogs
Jump to and fro.

3 Two little frogs
Sitting on a well,
Two leaned over
And down they fell.

Frogs jump high,
Frogs jump low,
No little frogs
Jump to and fro.

Today as I went out to play
I saw a brown frog in the way,
I know that frogs are smooth and green,
But this was brown – what could it mean?
I asked a lady in the road;
She said it was a spotted toad!

21 · spiders

I have a little spider,
I am very fond of him,
He climbs onto my shoulder
And then onto my chin.
He crawls down my arm
And jumps on my leg,
Now he's a tired little spider
So I put him into bed.

It's funny how beetles
and creatures like that
can walk upside down
as well as walk flat:

They crawl on a ceiling
and climb on a wall
without any practice
or trouble at all,

While I have been trying
for a year (maybe more)
and still I can't stand
with my head on the floor.

2 Incy Wincy spider was climbing up the trees,
Down came the snow and made the spider freeze.
Out came the sun and melted all the snow,
So Incy Wincy spider had another go!

and creepy crawlies

I saw a beetle
crawl – crawl – crawl –
I saw a beetle
crawling up the wall.

Slowly, slowly, very slowly
Creeps the garden snail,
Slowly, slowly, very slowly
Up the wooden rail.

A ladybird came on my hand
one day,
She stayed for a while – then
flew away.

I saw a slippery, slithery snake
Slide through the grasses making them shake.
He looked at me with his beady eye,
'Go away from my pretty green garden,' said I.
'Sssssssss,' said the slippery, slithery snake,
As he slid through the grasses making them shake.

Once I saw an ant hill,
With no ants about,
So I said, 'Dear little ants
Won't you please come out?'
Then as if the ants had
Heard my call
1, 2, 3, 4, 5 came out
But that was all.

22 · butterflies

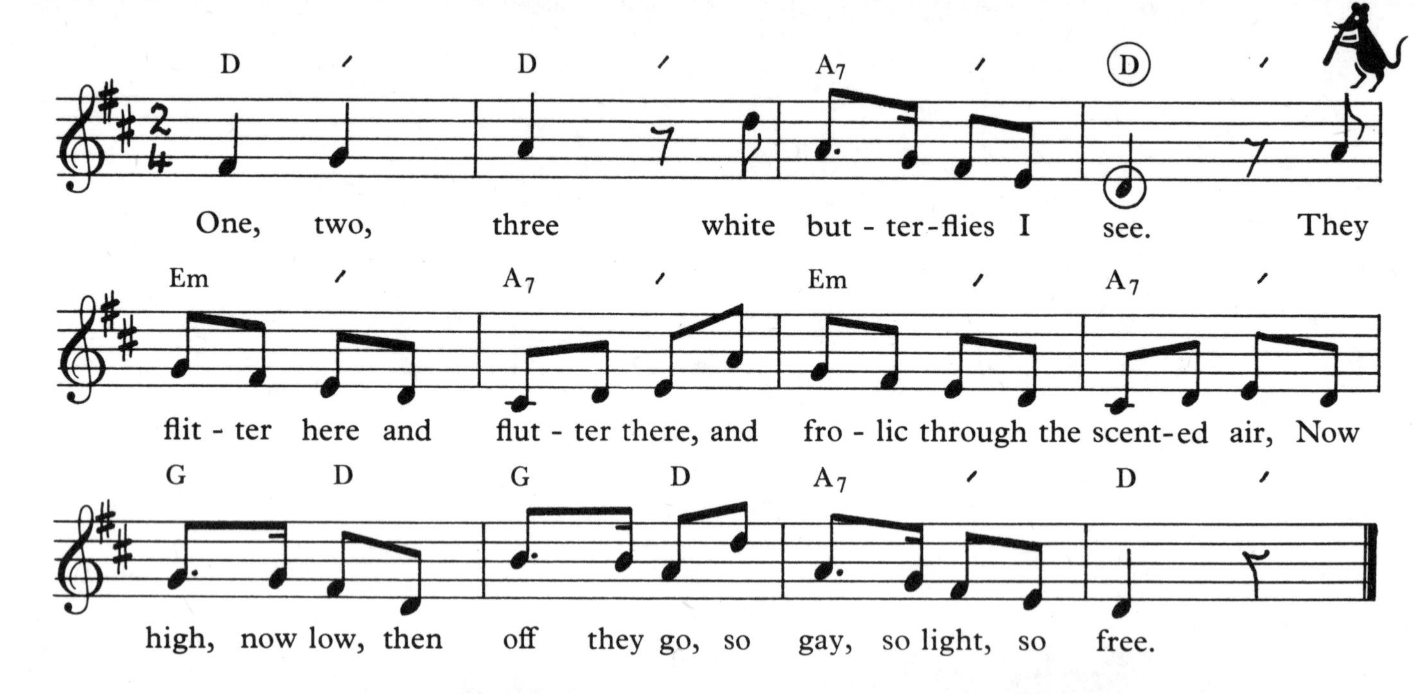

Butterfly, butterfly,
Why do you flutter by,
Butterfly, butterfly?

Butterfly, butterfly,
Where do you fly?
Butterfly, butterfly,
Bye—

I saw a caterpillar
crawl – crawl – crawl –
I saw a caterpillar
crawling up the wall.

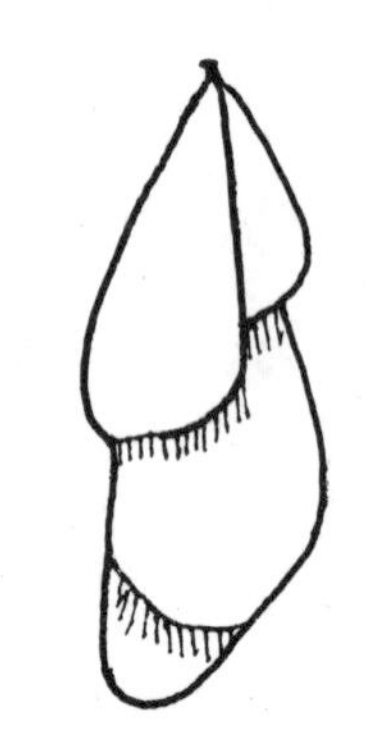

Little Arabella Miller
Found a furry caterpillar,
And let it crawl upon her mother,
Then upon her little brother.
Both cried 'Naughty Arabella,
Take away the caterpillar.'

I wish I was a little grub
With whiskers on my tummy.
I'd climb into the honey-pot,
And make my tummy gummy.
And then I'd crawl all over you
And make your tummy gummy, too.

and bees

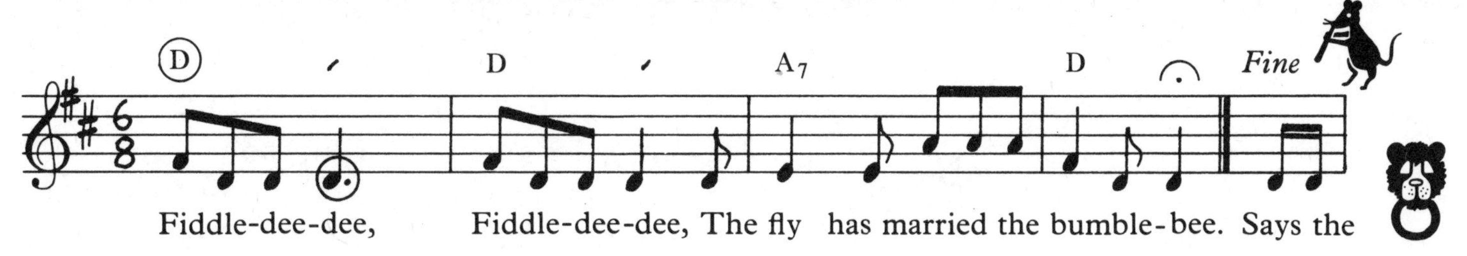

Here is the beehive,
Where are the bees?
Hiding inside where nobody sees.
Here they come creeping
Out of their hive;
One, two, three, four and five.
Buzz – buzz – buzz.

2 Says the bee, says she,
'I'll live under your wing,
And you'll never know
I carry a sting.'
Fiddle-dee-dee . . .

3 And the flies did buzz
And the bells did ring,
Did ever you hear
So merry a thing?
Fiddle-dee-dee . . .

What do you suppose?
A bee sat on my nose.
Then what do you think –
He gave me a wink
And said, 'I beg your pardon,
I thought you were the garden!'

Guess what is making the sound you hear:
zzz – zzz – zzz – zzz.
A bee is making the sound I hear.

Guess what is making the sound you hear:
sh – sh – sh – sh.
The sea is making the sound I hear.

(This rhyme can be changed for any sounds.)

'I'm busy, busy, busy,' said the bee,
'I shan't be home for dinner or for tea.
It makes me very dizzy,
To be so very busy,
I'm busy, busy, busy,' said the bee.

23 · birds

The owl has great big eyes and a pointed nose,
Two pointed ears and claws for toes,
He sits on a tree and looks at you,
Flaps his wings and says – 'Twit-ta-Whoo!'

Once I saw a little bird come
Hop, hop, hop.
And I cried 'Little bird will you
Stop, stop, stop?'
I was going to the window to say
'How do you do?'
But he shook his little tail
And away he flew.

The cuckoo comes in April,
Sings a song in May.
In the middle of June another tune
And then he flies away.

Eggs are laid by turkeys,
Eggs are laid by hens,
Eggs are laid by robins,
Eggs are laid by wrens,
Eggs are laid by eagles,
Eggs are laid by quail,
Pigeons, parrots, peregrines:
And that's how every bird begins.

Fly away, fly away, over the sea,
Sun-loving swallow, for summer is done.
Come again, come again, come back to me,
Bringing the summer and bringing the sun.

My poor old bones – I've only two,
A broomstick and a broken stave,
My ragged gloves are a disgrace,
My one peg-foot is in the grave.

I wear the labourer's old clothes,
Coat, shirt and trousers all undone.
I bear my cross upon a hill
In rain and shine, in snow and sun.

I cannot help the way I look,
My funny hat is full of hay.
O, wild birds, come and nest in me –
Why do you always fly away?

Little Robin Redbreast sat upon a rail,
Niddle, naddle went his head,
Wiggle, waggle went his tail.
'Little Rob Robin, where do you live?'
'Up in yonder wood, sir, on a hazel twig.'

2 The north wind doth blow,
And we shall have snow,
And what will the swallow do then, Poor thing?
Oh, do you not know
That he's off long ago,
To a country where he will find spring, Poor thing!

3 The north wind doth blow,
And we shall have snow,
And what will the dormouse do then, Poor thing?
Roll'd up like a ball,
In the nest snug and small,
He'll sleep till warm weather comes in, Poor thing!

4 The north wind doth blow,
And we shall have snow,
And what will the honey-bee do then, Poor thing?
In his hive he will stay
Till the cold is away,
And then he'll come out in the spring, Poor thing!

5 The north wind doth blow,
And we shall have snow,
And what will the children do then, Poor things?
When lessons are done,
They must skip, jump, and run,
Until they have made themselves warm, Poor things!

24 · when is it?

Monday alone,
Tuesday together,
Wednesday we walk
When it's fine weather,
Thursday we kiss,
Friday we cry,
Saturday's hours
Seem almost to fly.
But of all the days
Of the week we will call
Sunday the rest day,
The best day of all.

March winds and April showers,
Bring forth May flowers.

Monday's child is fair of face,
Tuesday's child is full of grace,
Wednesday's child is full of woe,
Thursday's child has far to go,
Friday's child is loving and giving,
Saturday's child works hard for his living,
And the child that is born on the Sabbath day
Is bonny and blithe, and good and gay.

Thirty days hath September,
April, June and November;
All the rest have thirty-one,
February has twenty-eight alone,
Except in leap year. That's the time
When February's days are twenty-nine.

January brings the snow,
Makes our feet and fingers glow.

February brings the rain,
Thaws the frozen ponds again.

March brings breezes loud and shrill,
Stirs the dancing daffodil.

April brings the primrose sweet,
Scatters daisies at our feet.

May brings flocks of pretty lambs,
Skipping by their fleecy dams.

June brings tulips, lilies, roses,
Fills the children's hands with posies.

Hot July brings cooling showers,
Apricots and gilly flowers.

August brings the sheaves of corn,
Then the harvest load is born.

Warm September brings the fruit,
Sportsmen then begin to shoot.

Fresh October brings the pheasant,
Then to gather nuts is pleasant.

Dull November brings the blast,
Then the leaves are whirling fast.

Chill December brings the sleet,
Blazing fire and Christmas treat.

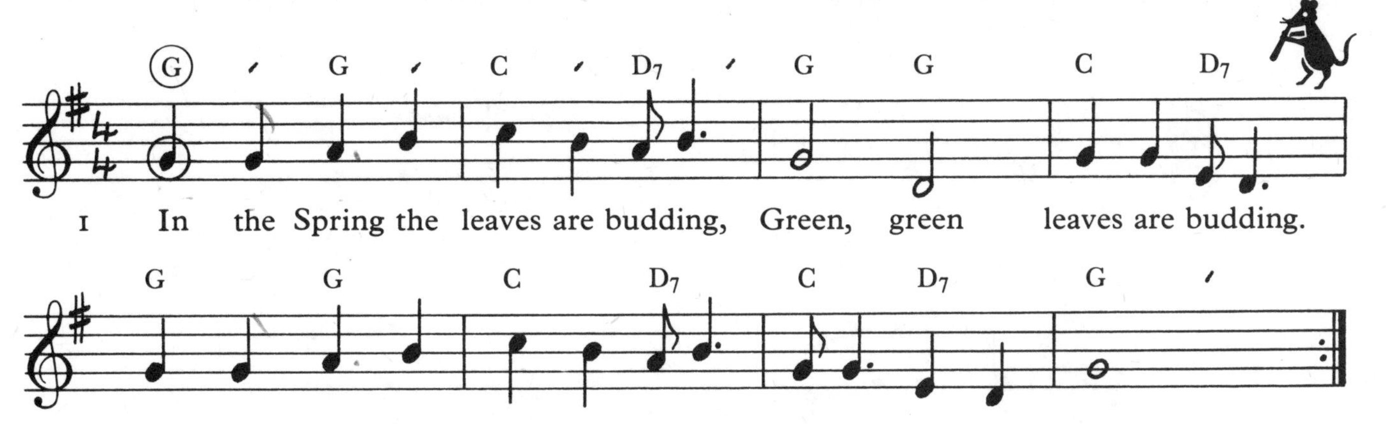

2 In the Summer leaves are rustling,
Green, green leaves are rustling.
In the Summer leaves are rustling,
Rustling on the trees.

3 In the Autumn leaves are falling,
Brown, brown leaves are falling.
In the Autumn leaves are falling,
Falling from the trees.

4 In the Winter leaves are sleeping,
Brown, brown leaves are sleeping.
In the winter leaves are sleeping,
Sleeping in the trees.

The leaves are green,
The nuts are brown,
They hang so high
They will not come down.

Leave them alone
Till frosty weather,
Then they will all
Come down together.

I like to think
That, long ago,
There fell to earth
Some flakes of snow
Which loved this cold,
Grey world of ours
So much, they stayed
As snowdrop flowers.

Winter is the king of showmen,
Turning tree stumps into snowmen
And houses into birthday cakes
And spreading sugar over the lakes.
Smooth and clean and frost white
The world looks good enough to bite.
That's the season to be young,
Catching snowflakes on your tongue.

Snow is snowy when it's snowing,
I'm sorry it's slushy when it's going.

25 · the wind, sun,

2 Good morning Mister Sun, I hope you're feeling fine,
The day has just begun, it's time for you to shine.
Good morning, Good morning, Good morning, Mister Sun.

No one can tell me,
Nobody knows,
Where the wind comes from,
Where the wind goes.

It's flying from somewhere
As fast as it can,
I couldn't keep up with it,
Not if I ran.

But if I stopped holding
The string of my kite,
It would blow with the wind
For a day and a night.

And then when I found it,
Wherever it blew,
I should know that the wind
Had been going there too.

So then I could tell them
Where the wind goes . . .
But where the wind comes from
Nobody knows.

White sheep, white sheep
On a blue hill,
When the wind stops
You all stand still.

You all run away
When the winds blow;
White sheep, white sheep,
Where do you go?

Rumbling in the chimneys,
Rattling at the doors,
Round the roofs and round the roads
The rude wind roars;
Raging through the darkness
Raving through the trees,
Racing off again across
The great grey seas.

and snow

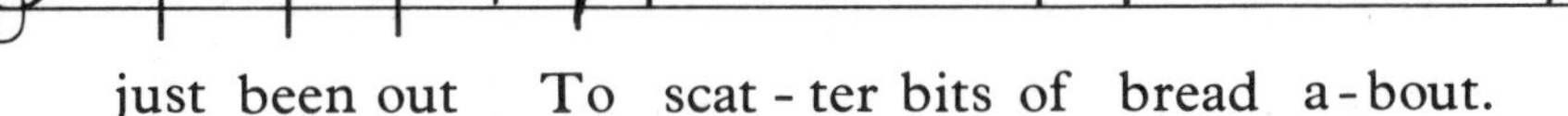

2 One little sparrow was out today,
He ate some bread and hopped away . . .*chorus*

3 A pigeon ate some breadcrumbs too,
He walked around, then off he flew . . .*chorus*

4 A cat crept up behind the hedge,
Then sprang on to the window ledge . . .*chorus*

5 A squirrel found the snow too deep,
So went off home to have some sleep . . .*chorus*

6 On his horse, the farmer's son,
Went riding off to have some fun.

Snow, snow,
snow no more!
You've iced our window
and blocked our door.
The snow has melted
and soaked our floor.
Snow, snow,
snow no more!

26 · and rain...

Rain, rain, go away
Come again another day.

Rain, rain, pour down
But not a drop on our town.

Rain, rain, go to Spain,
Never show your face again.

2 I see blue skies, I see blue skies, Way up high, way up high,
Hurry up the sunshine, Hurry up the sunshine, I'll soon dry, So will I.

Pitter-patter,
Pitter-patter,
Listen to the rain.
Pitter-patter,
Pitter-patter,
On the window pane.

Marching in our Wellingtons,
Tramp, tramp, tramp,
Marching in our Wellingtons,
We won't get damp.

Splashing through the puddles
In the rain, rain, rain –
Splashing through the puddles,
And splashing home again!

Pitter-pat, pitter-pat,
What was that?
What was that?
One big raindrop on my hat.

It's raining, it's pouring,
The old man is snoring!
He went to bed and bumped his head,
And couldn't get up in the morning.

...again

There is no colour in the rain,
It's only water, wet and plain.
It makes damp spots upon my book
And splashes on my new dress, look!
But puddles, in the rainy weather,
Glisten like a peacock's feather.

The wind has such a rainy sound,
Moaning through the town,
The sea has such a windy sound –
Will the ships go down?

The apples in the orchard
Tumble from their tree –
Oh will the ships go down, go down,
In the windy sea?

Misty, moisty was the morn,
Chilly was the weather;
There I met an old man
Dressed all in leather –

Dressed all in leather
Against the wind and rain,
With 'How do you do?' and 'How do you do?'
And 'How do you do?' again.

'Who is tapping at my window?'
'It's not I,' said the cat.
'Who is tapping at my window?'
'It's not I,' said the cat.
'It's not I,' said the rat.
'It's not I,' said the wren.
'It's not I,' said the hen.
'It's not I,' said the fox.
'It's not I,' said the ox.
'It's not I,' said the dog.
'It's not I,' said the frog.
'It's not I,' said the hare.
'It's not I,' said the bear.
'It is I,' said the rain,
'Tapping on your windowpane.'

MD

Doctor Foster went to Gloucester
In a shower of rain.
He stepped in a puddle
Right up to his middle
And never went there again.

27 · singing

I wake in the morning early,
And always the very first thing
I sit up in bed and I poke out my head
And I sing, and I sing, and I sing.

As I was going along, along, along,
A-singing a comical song, song, song,
The lane that I went was so long, long, long,
And the song that I sang was so long, long, long,
That the words and the music went wrong, wrong, wrong,
As I went singing along.

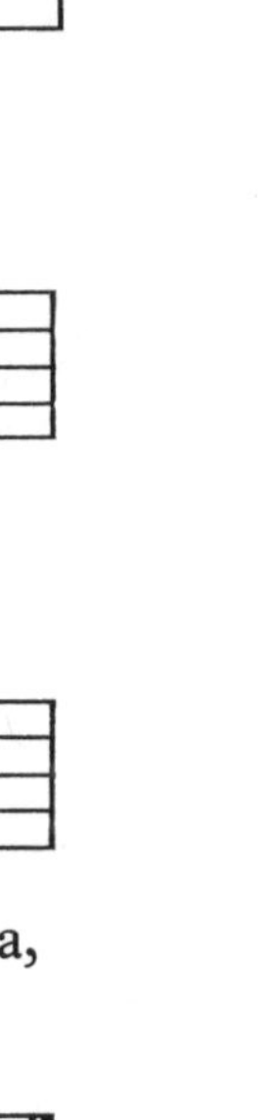

My grandmother said, 'Now isn't it queer,
That boys must whistle and girls must sing?
But that's how 'tis!' I heard her say –
'The same tomorrow as yesterday.'

Grandmother said, when I asked her why
Girls couldn't whistle the same as I,
'Son, you know it's a natural thing –
Boys just whistle, and girls just sing.'

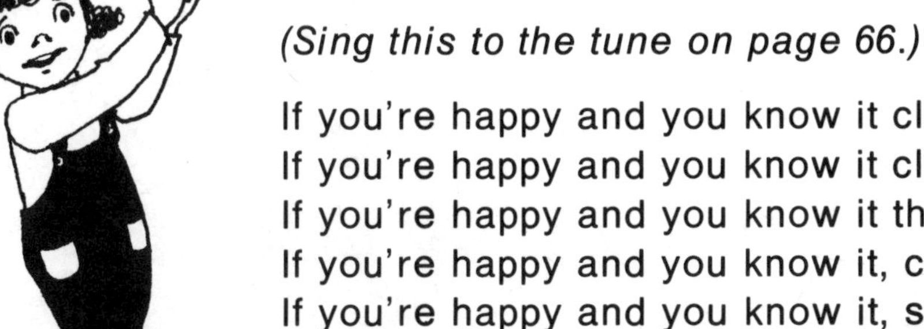

(Sing this to the tune on page 66.)

If you're happy and you know it clap your hands, (*clap, clap*)
If you're happy and you know it clap your hands, (*clap, clap*)
If you're happy and you know it then you surely want to show it,
If you're happy and you know it, clap your hands. (*clap, clap*)
If you're happy and you know it, stamp your feet (*stamp, stamp*) . . .
If you're happy and you know it, shout 'We are!' (*We are!*) . . .
If you're happy and you know it, do all three.

(clap clap, stamp stamp, 'We are!') . . .

28 • me-growing

C
G
one year old - er now, then in one year on from now, I'll be

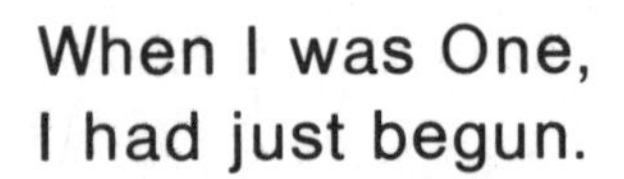

When I was One,
I had just begun.

When I was Two,
I was nearly new.

When I was Three,
I was hardly Me.

When I was Four,
I was not much more.

When I was Five,
I was just alive.

But now I am Six, I'm as clever as clever,
So I think I'll be six for ever and ever.

I looked in the mirror
and looked at my nose:
it's the funniest thing,
the way it grows
stuck right out where all of it shows
with two little holes where the
breathing goes.

I looked in the mirror
and saw in there
the end of my chin
and the start of my hair
and between there isn't much space to spare
with my nose, like a handle,
sticking there.

If ever you want
to giggle and shout
and can't think of what
to do it about,
just look in the mirror and then, no doubt,
you'll see how funny **your** nose
sticks out!

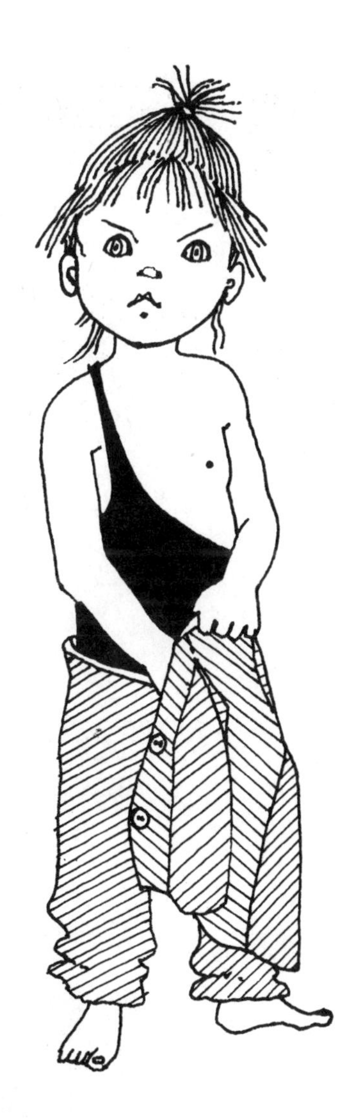

Yesterday
I had some thoughts
of Mummy
making me wear shorts.
I know it's hot
but I will not!

Isn't dressing depressing?

Button the buttons
Snap the snaps
Hook the hooks and
Zip the zippers
Tie the ties and
Strap the straps and
Clasp the clasps and
Slip the slippers
Buckle the buckles and
Knot the knots and
Pin the pins and
Lace the laces
Loop the loops and
Lock the locks and
Belt the belts and
Brace the braces –

What I like best is my own skin –
That is the dress I'm always in.

29 · when I grow up

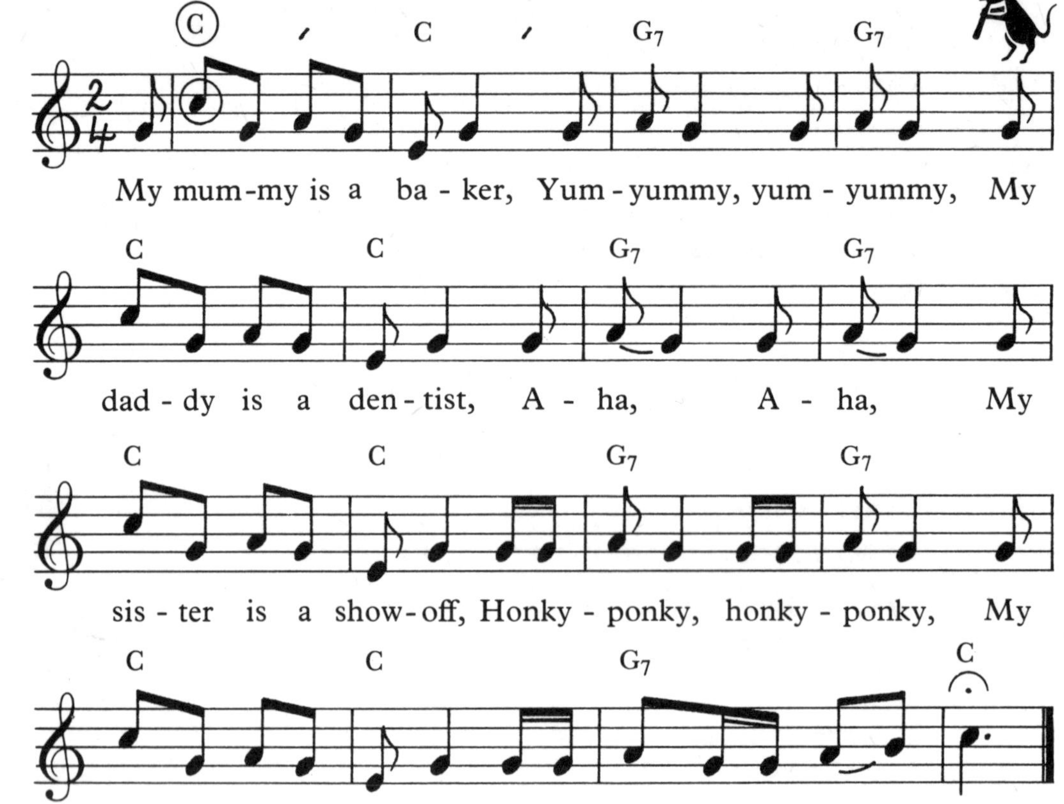

Tinker, tailor, soldier, sailor,
Rich man, poor man, ploughboy, thief.
And what about a cowboy,
Policeman, Jailer,
Engine-driver,
Or Pirate Chief?

What about a postman – or a keeper
  at the Zoo?
What about the circus man who lets
  the people through?
And the man who takes the pennies
  for the roundabouts and swings?
Or the man who plays the organ, and
  the other man who sings?
What about a conjurer with rabbits in
  his pockets?
What about a rocket man who's always making
  rockets?
Oh, there's such a lot of things to do and such a lot to be
That there's always lots of cherries on my little cherry tree!

Every Thursday morning
Before we're quite awake,
Without the slightest warning
The house begins to shake
  With a Biff! Bang!
  Biff! Bang! Biff!
It's the Dustman, who begins
  Bang! Crash!
To empty all the bins
Of their rubbish and their ash
  With a Biff! Bang!
  Biff! Bang! Bash!

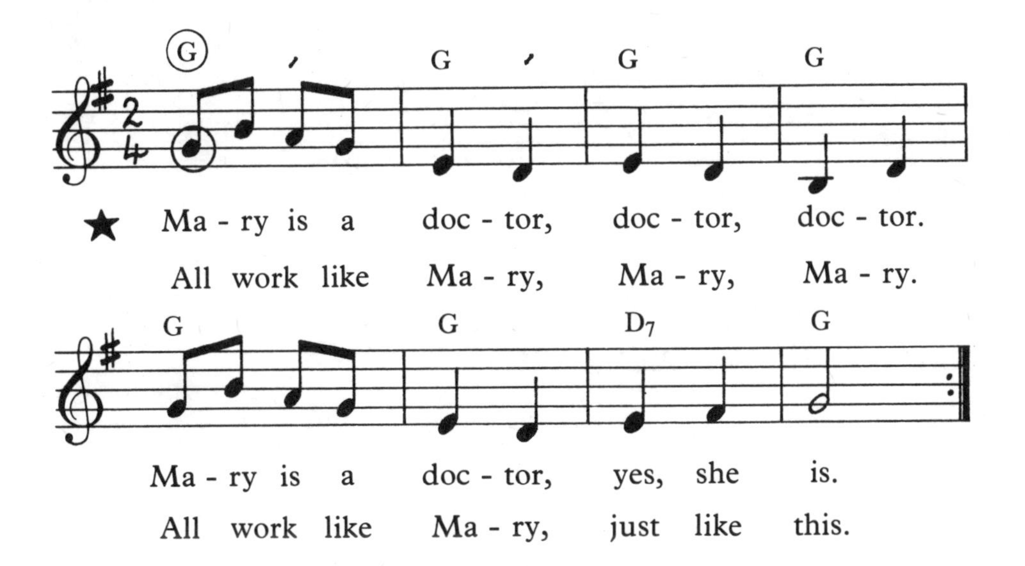

★ *(Let the children sing their own names and make up their own verses and jobs.)*

Sing this song to the same tune:

★ Johnny, get your hair cut, hair cut, hair cut.
Johnny, get your hair cut, just like me.

Watch the policeman in the street
Move his arms but not his feet;
He only has to raise his hand,
Cars and buses understand.
He can make them stop and go,
He can move them to and fro.
Watch the policeman in the street
Move his arms but not his feet.

I'd like to be a barber, and learn to shave and clip,
Calling out, 'Next, please!' and pocketing my tip.
All day you'd hear my scissors going, 'Snip, Snip, Snip!'

I'd lather people's faces, and their noses I would grip
While I shaved most carefully along the upper lip.
But I wouldn't be a barber if —
The razor was to slip –
Would you?

30 · lots of jobs

2 His caravan has windows two,
And a chimney of tin that the smoke comes through.
He has a wife and a baby brown,
And they go riding from town to town.

3 Chairs to mend and delf to sell –
He clashes the basins like a bell.
Tea-trays, baskets, ranged in order,
Plates, with the alphabet round the border.

4 The roads are brown, and the sea is green,
But his house is just like a bathing-machine.
The world is round, but he can ride,
Rumble, and splash to the other side.

5 With the pedlar-man I should like to roam,
And write a book when I come home.
All the people would read my book,
Just like the Travels of Captain Cook.

and clocks

A dillar, a dollar,
A ten o'clock scholar,
What makes you come so soon?
You used to come at ten o'clock,
And now you come at noon.

Cobbler, cobbler, mend my shoe,
Get it done by half-past two,
Half-past two is much too late,
Get it done by half-past eight.

Every morning at nine o'clock
You can hear the postman's knock, knock, knock.
Up jumps ★ to open the door,
One letter, two letters, three letters, four.

When I grow up I want to be
A window cleaning man,
And make the windows in our street
As shiny as I can.
I'll put my ladder by the wall
And up the steps I'll go,
But when I'm up there with my pail
I hope the wind won't blow.

Rat-a-tat-tat, rat-a-tat-tat,
Rat-a-tat-tat, tattoo.
That's the way the postman goes,
Rat-a-tat-tat, tattoo.
Every morning at half-past eight
You hear him open the garden gate
With a rat-a-tat-tat, rat-a-tat-tat,
Rat-a-tat-tat, tattoo.

Our milkman's name is Mr Brown,
He drives his van around the town,
And leaves the milk inside the gate,
When all the clocks are striking eight.
1, 2, 3, 4, 5, 6, 7, 8 (*claps*)

There was a king who had four sons,
For breakfast they had currant buns,
It seems a funny thing to me,
But every day they each ate three.
Every day the baker came,
Every day it was the same,
Every day at half-past eight
He left twelve buns at the castle gate.

Every morning at eight o'clock
You can hear the milkman's knock, knock, knock.
Up jumps ★ to open the door,
One bottle, two bottles, three bottles, four.

31 · cowboys...

2 They've ploughed and fenced my cattle range,
And the people there are all so strange.

3 I'll take my horse, I'll take my rope,
And hit the trail upon a lope.

4 Say adios to the Alamo
And turn my head toward Mexico.

Cowboy Joe from Mexico,
Hands up, stick 'em up,
Drop your guns and pick 'em up.

...and pirates

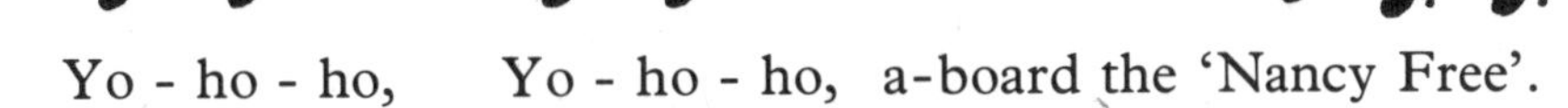

One-eyed Jack, the pirate chief,
Was a terrible, fearsome ocean thief.
He wore a peg
Upon one leg;
He wore a hook –
And a dirty look!
One-eyed Jack, the pirate chief,
A terrible, fearsome ocean thief.

2 Many merchant ships he found, and many ships he sank.
And those who met the Nancy Free were made to walk the plank.
Splosh, splosh, splosh, splosh, were made to walk the plank.

3 Captain Patch was awful fierce and so were all his crew.
But they kept leaving things behind, and that you musn't do.
Yo ho ho, yo ho ho, and that you musn't do.

4 One day they leapt aboard an English ship of forty tons.
And they were so forgetful they forgot to bring their guns.
Yo ho ho, yo ho ho, forgot to bring their guns.

5 The English captain jumped for joy: 'Arrest those men' said he.
'We've captured Captain Patch and all his crew of fifty-three.
Yo ho ho, yo ho ho, his crew of fifty-three.'

6 'What a silly blunder for such pirates bold to make.
Now we'll make them walk the plank to pay for their mistake.
Splosh, splosh, splosh, splosh, to pay for their mistake.'

7 That's the end of Captain Patch and all his pirate larks.
His end delighted everyone, including lots of sharks.
Yo ho ho, yo ho ho, including lots of sharks.

32 · sailors

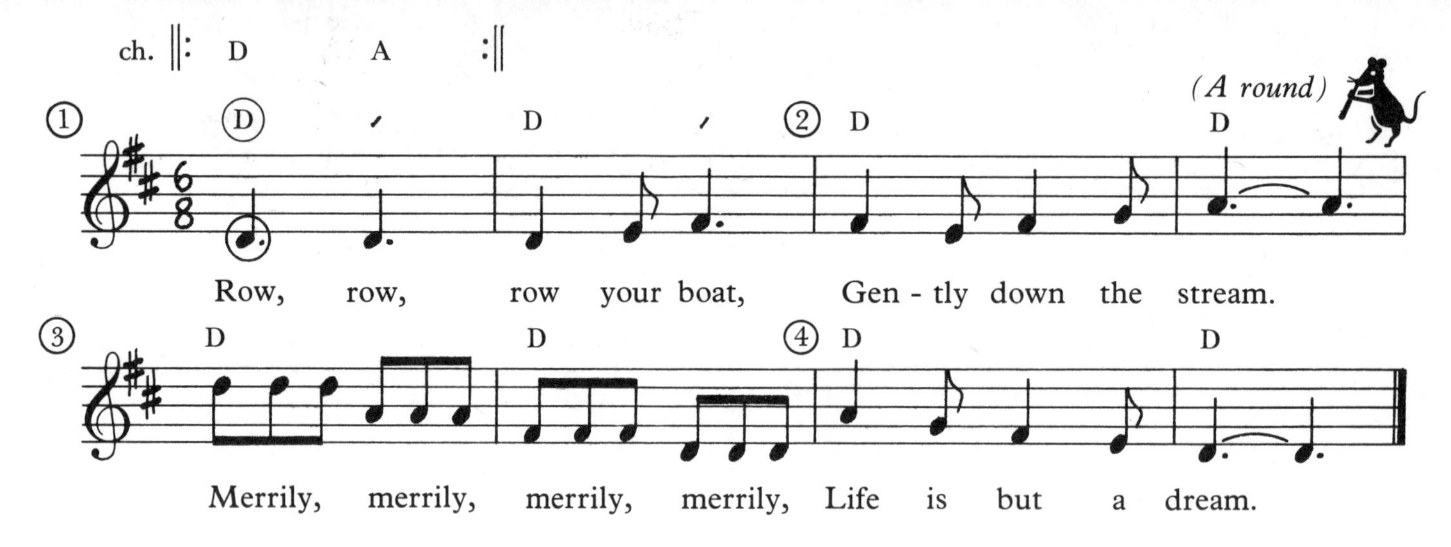

Have you seen the boat leave?
It sails each day at three.
The engines whirr, the siren whines
And then it's off to sea.

The tide in the river,
The tide in the river,
The tide in the river runs deep,
I saw a shiver
Pass over the river
As the tide turned in its sleep.

'Ferry me across the water,
Do, boatman, do.'
'If you've a penny in your purse
I'll ferry you.'

'I have a penny in my purse,
And my eyes are blue;
So ferry me across the water
Do, boatman, do.'

'Step into my ferry-boat,
Be they black or blue,
And for the penny in your purse
I'll ferry you.'

Blue is the sea,
Green is the grass,
White are the clouds
As they slowly pass.
Black are the crows,
Brown are the trees,
Red are the sails
Of a ship in the breeze.

1 Michael's boat is a music boat. Al-le-lu-ia.
Michael's boat is a music boat. Al-le-lu-ia.

2 Sister help to trim the sail, Al-le-lu-ia.
Sister help to trim the sail, Al-le-lu-ia.

'Hullo, sailor!'
'Hullo, man!'
'Bring me a coconut!'
'Yes, if I can;

'I'll bring you a sword
And a silken fan!'
'Goodbye, sailor!'
'Goodbye, man!'

There are big waves and little waves,
Green waves and blue.
Waves you can jump over,
Waves you dive through,
Waves that rise up
Like a great water wall,
Waves that swell softly
And don't break at all,
Waves that can whisper,
Waves that can roar,
And tiny waves that run at you
Running on the shore.

If all the seas were one sea,
What a great sea that would be!
If all the trees were one tree,
What a great tree that would be!
And if all the axes were one axe,
What a great axe that would be!
And if all the men were one man,
What a great man that would be!
And if the great man took the great axe,
And cut down the great tree,
And let it fall into the great sea,
What a splish-splash that would be!

33 · the sea

Sea Shell, Sea Shell,
Sing me a song, O Please!
A song of ships, and sailor men,
And parrots, and tropical trees.
Of islands lost in the Spanish Main
Which no man ever may find again,
Of fishes and corals under the waves,
And sea horses stabled in great green caves.
Sea Shell, Sea Shell,
Sing of the things you know so well.

I made a sand castle.
In rolled the sea.
'All sand castles
belong to me –
to me,'
said the sea.

I dug sand tunnels.
In flowed the sea.
'All sand tunnels
belong to me –
to me,'
said the sea.

I saw my sand pail floating free.
I ran and snatched it from the sea.
'My sand pail
belongs to me – to **me**!'

The sea is a hungry dog,
Giant and grey.
He rolls on the beach all day.
With his clashing teeth and shaggy jaws
Hour upon hour he gnaws
The rumbling, tumbling stones,
And 'Bones, bones, bones, bones!'
The giant sea-dog moans,
Licking his greasy paws.

And when the night wind roars
And the moon rocks in the stormy cloud,
He bounds to his feet and snuffs and sniffs,
Shaking his wet sides over the cliffs,
And howls and hollows long and loud.

But on quiet days in May or June,
When even the grasses on the dune
Play no more their reedy tune,
With his head between his paws
He lies on the sandy shores,
So quiet, so quiet, he scarcely snores.

When I was down beside the sea,
A wooden spade they gave to me
To dig the sandy shore.

My holes were empty like a cup.
In every hole the sea came up
Till it could come no more.

and submarines

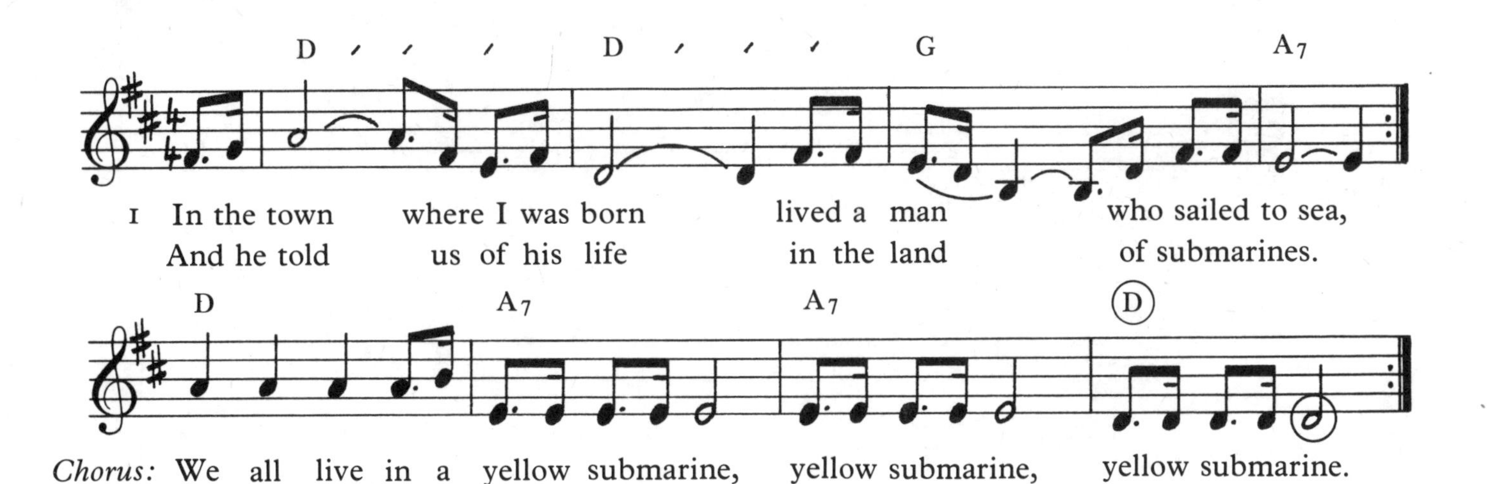

2 So we sailed up to the sun till we found the sea of green,
And we lived beneath the waves in our yellow submarine.

3 And our friends are all aboard, many more of them live next door,
And the band begins to play . . .
(pom, pom, pom, pom, pom, pom, pom, pom, pom!)

4 As we live a life of ease, every one of us has all we need.
Sky of blue and sea of green in our yellow submarine.

34 · up in the air...

rrrrrrrrrr The engine roars,
The propeller spins,
'Close the doors!'
Our flight begins.

zzzzzzzzzz The plane rises;
It skims the trees.
Over the houses
We fly at our ease.

The aeroplane taxies down the field
And heads into the breeze,
It lifts its wheels above the ground,
It skims above the trees.
It rises high and higher,
Away up toward the sun,
It's just a speck against the sky –
And now it's gone.

2 I would like to ride in your beautiful balloon,
I would like to ride in your beautiful balloon,
We could sing a song and sail along
in the silver sky, for we can fly,
Up, up and away in this beautiful balloon.

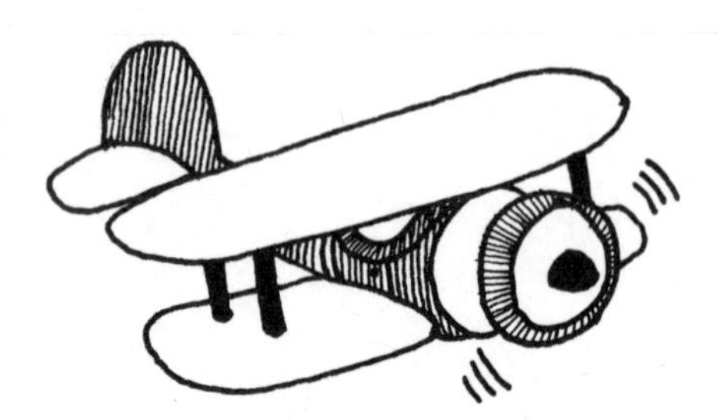

mmmmmmmmmm ZOOM goes the plane,
The engine hums.
Then home again,
And down it comes . . .

...and into space

'Flying man, flying man up in the sky,
Where are you going to, flying so high?'
'Over the mountain, over the sea.'
'Flying man, flying man,
Can't you take me?'

What's the news of the day,
Good neighbour, I pray?
They say a balloon
Has gone up to the moon.

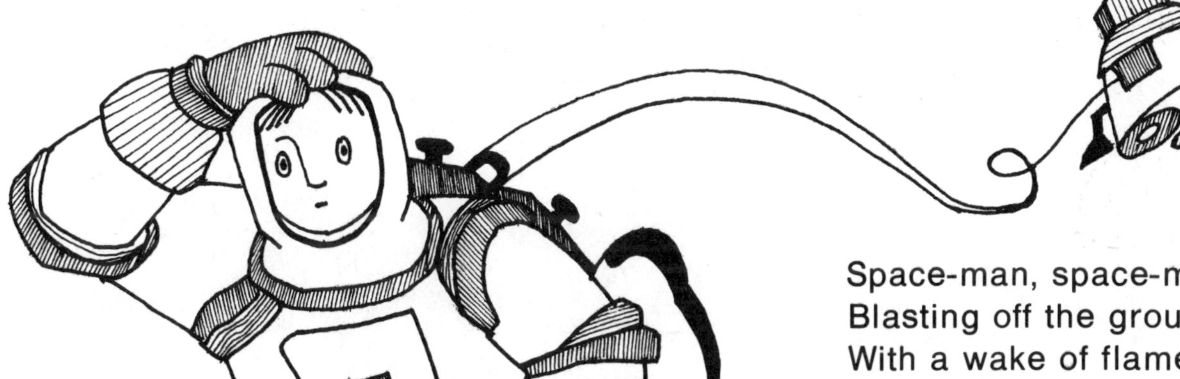

Space-man, space-man,
Blasting off the ground;
With a wake of flame behind you,
Swifter than passing sound.

Space-man, ace-man,
Shooting through the air,
Twice around the moon and back
Simply because it's there.

Space-man, place-man,
Cruising through the skies
To plant your flags on landscapes
Unknown to human eyes.

Space-man – Race, man,
Scorching back to earth –
To home and friends and everything
That gives your mission worth.

Boom off!
Zoom off!
Now we're on our way.
Our rocket's left the launching pad
And we're in space today.

Drop down!
Plop down!
Get the buggy out.
It's just the thing upon the moon
To help us get about.

Crash down!
Splash down!
We go back to a ship,
With cheers and claps and handshakes
To end our first moon trip.

35 · trains

Let it rain!
Who cares?
I've a train
Upstairs,
With a brake
Which I make
From a string
Sort of thing,
Which works
In jerks,
'Cos it drops
In the spring,
Which stops
With the string,
And the wheels
All stick
So quick
That it feels
Like a thing
That you make
With a brake,
Not string . . .
So that's what I make,
When the day's all wet.
It's a good sort of brake
But it hasn't worked yet.

(Start slowly, gradually getting faster.)

Cof-fee, cof-fee,
Cheese and biscuits, cheese and biscuits,
Plums and custard, plums and custard,
Beef and carrots, beef and carrots,
Fish and chips, fish and chips,
Sou—p.

2 Better get your tickets, O – Yes . . .
3 Going through a tunnel, O – Yes . . .
4 Stopping at the station, O – Yes . . .

The train goes running along the line.
Jicketty-can, jicketty-can.
I wish it were mine, I wish it were mine,
Jicketty-can, jicketty-can.
The engine driver stands in front –
He makes it run, he makes it shunt.
Out of the town,
Out of the town,
Over the hill,
Over the down.
Under the bridges,
Across the lea,
Over the ridges,
And down to the sea.
With a jicketty-can, jicketty-can,
jicketty-jicketty-jicketty-can.

Here is the train . . .
here is the train.
Let us get in . . .
Let us get in.
Where shall we sit . . .
When will it go . . .
Wave the flag . . .
Off we go . . .
What can we see . . .
Look at the cows . . .
Isn't it fun . . .
Going along . . .
Hurrying on . . .
Nearly there . . .
There's the sea . . .
Look at the ships . . .
Here we are . . .
Out we get . . .
Tickets please!

2 In eighteen hundred and forty-two,
I left the old world for the new.
'Twas my bad luck that brought me through,
to work upon the railway.

3 It's 'Pat, do this' and 'Pat, do that',
Without a stocking or cravat,
Nothing but an old straw hat,
to work upon the railway.

36 · buses, cars...

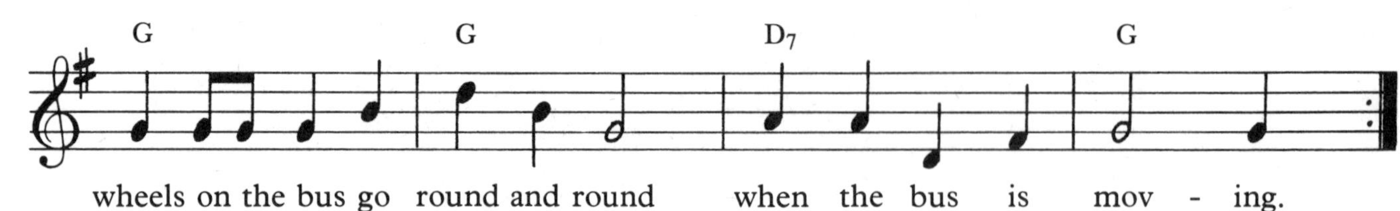

2 The conductor on the bus says, ‘Tickets, please’ . . .

3 The bell on the bus goes ‘Ting, ting ting’ . . .

4 The horn on the bus goes, ‘Peep, peep, peep’ . . .

5 The ladies on the bus go, ‘Chatter, chatter, chatter’ . . .

6 The men on the bus go nod, nod, nod . . .

7 The children on the bus go wriggle, wriggle, wriggle . . .

8 The babies on the bus go, ‘Eerr, eerr, eerr’ *(crying!)* . . .

9 The people on the bus bounce up and down . . .

There is a painted bus,
With twenty painted seats.
It carries painted people
Along the painted streets.
They pull the painted bell,
The painted driver stops,
And they all get out together
At the little painted shops.

My motor is humming,
I’m coming, I’m coming,
Make room, make room, make room!
Not a minute to wait,
I’m late, I’m late,
Make room, make room, make room!

Flicker-flicker-flack, flicker-flicker-flack.
The wipers on the car go
flicker-flicker-flack.
The rain goes flick, the rain goes flack.
The wipers on the car go
flicker-flicker-flack.

...and bicycles

One wheel on a barrow (painted red and blue),
Two wheels on my scooter, and on my cycle too.

Three wheels on a tricycle, but that's too small for me!
Four wheels on a motor car, as anyone can see.

Six wheels on a trolleybus – it's fun to take a ride;
And eight wheels on a lorry that's long and very wide.

37 · witches

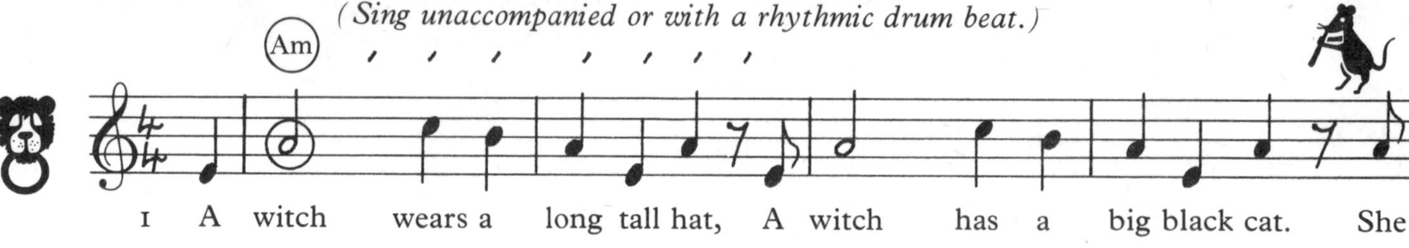

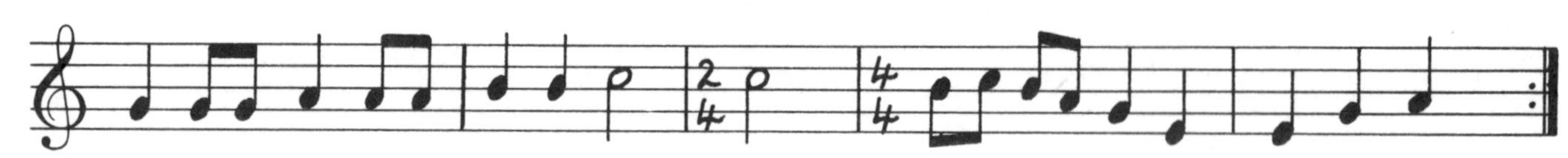

2 A witch wears long black hair.
A witch flies through the air.
She sits on a broomstick as she goes by
And 'Oo-oo-oo-oo-oo-ooh' is her cry.

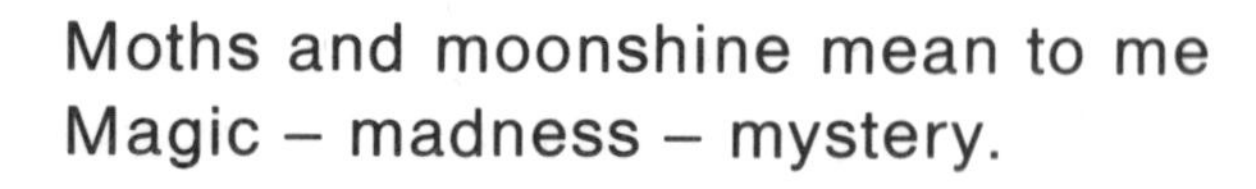

Moths and moonshine mean to me
Magic – madness – mystery.

Witches dancing weird and wild
Mischief make for man and child.

Owls screech from woodland shades,
Moths glide through moonlit glades,

Moving in dark and secret wise
Like a plotter in disguise.

Moths and moonshine mean to me
Magic – madness – mystery.

'Abracadabra, wizzy woo
I can fly and so can you.'

'Double, double, toil and trouble,
Fire burn and cauldron bubble.'

2 We're witches of Hallowe'en – Woo-oo,
Our faces are crooked and green – Woo-oo,
We have black pointed hats
And wicked witches' cats,
We're witches of Hallowe'en – Woo-oo.

'Witch, witch, where do you fly?'
'Under the clouds and over the sky.'

'Witch, witch, what do you eat?'
'Little black apples from Hurricane Street.'

'Witch, witch, what do you drink?'
'Vinegar, blacking and good red ink.'

'Witch, witch, where do you sleep?'
'Up in the clouds where pillows are cheap.'

There was an old woman tossed up in a basket
Nineteen times as high as the moon.
Where she was going I couldn't but ask it,
For in her hand she carried a broom.

'Old woman, old woman, old woman,' quoth I,
'O whither, O whither, O whither, so high?'
'To brush the cobwebs off the sky!'
'Shall I go with you?' 'Aye, by and by.'

38 · funny people

Chorus: And he played upon a ladle, a ladle, a ladle,
And he played upon a ladle,
And his name was Aiken Drum.

2 And his hat was made of good cream cheese . . .
And his name was Aiken Drum.

3 And his coat was made of good roast beef . . .
And his name was Aiken Drum.

4 And his trousers were made of haggis bags . . .
And his name was Aiken Drum.

The man in the moon
Came down too soon
And asked his way to Norwich;
He went by the south
And burnt his mouth,
With eating cold plum porridge.

Rub-a-dub-dub,
Three men in a tub,
And how do you think they got there?
The butcher, the baker,
The candlestick-maker,
They all jumped out of a rotten potato,
'Twas enough to make a man stare.

Oh, Jemima, look at your Uncle Jim,
He's in the duckpond, learning how to swim.
First he does the breast-stroke,
Then he does the side,
Now he's under the water,
Swimming against the tide.

Have you heard of the man
Who stood on his head,
And put his clothes
Into his bed,
And folded himself
On a chair instead?

One day a boy went walking,
And walked into a store.
He bought a pound of sausages
And laid them on the floor.
The boy began to whistle,
He whistled up a tune,
And all the little sausages
Danced around the room.

Old John Muddlecombe lost his cap,
He couldn't find it anywhere, the poor old chap.
He walked down the High Street and everyone said,
'Silly John Muddlecombe, you've got it on your head.'

There was an old man with a beard,
Who said, 'It is just as I feared –
Two owls and a hen, four larks and a wren,
Have all built their nests in my beard!'

Mrs White had a fright
In the middle of the night.
She saw a ghost eating toast,
Half-way up a lamp-post.

Riddle cum diddle cum dido,
My little dog's name is Fido;
I bought him a wagon,
And hitched up a dragon,
And off we both went for a ride, oh!

Riddle cum diddle cum doodle,
My little cat's name is Toodle;
I curled up her hair
But she only said, 'There!
You have made me look just like a poodle!'

Riddle cum diddle cum dinky,
My little pig's name is Winky;
I keep him quite clean
With the washing machine,
And I rinse him all off in the sinkie.

When I went out for a walk one day,
My head fell off and rolled away,
And when I saw that it was gone –
I picked it up and put it on.

When I went into the street
Someone shouted, 'Look at your feet!'
I looked at them and sadly said,
'I've left them both asleep in bed.'

Sam, Sam, the dirty old man,
Washed his face in a frying pan,
Brushed his hair with a donkey's tail
And scratched his tummy with his big toe-nail.

One fine day in the middle of the night,
Two dead men got up to fight.
Back to back they faced each other,
Drew their swords and shot each other.

Hickory, dickory, dare,
A pig flew up in the air.
A man called Brown
Soon fetched him down.
Hickory, dickory, dare.

Higglety, pigglety, pop!
The dog has eaten the mop;
The pig's in a hurry,
The cat's in a flurry,
Higglety, pigglety, pop!

39 · funny words...

She sells sea-shells
On the sea-shore.

2 There was an old man called Michael Finnigin,
He went fishing with a pinigin,
He caught a fish but dropped it inigin,
Poor old Michael Finnigin. (Beginigin.)

Swan, swan, over the sea,
Swim, swan, swim.
Swan, swan, back again,
Well swum swan.

3 There was an old man called Michael Finnigin,
He grew fat and then grew thinigin,
Then he died – and had to beginigin,
Poor old Michael Finnigin – STOP!

Round and round the rugged rocks
The ragged rascal ran.

Red lorry, yellow lorry,
Red lorry, yellow lorry.

Red leather, yellow leather,
Red leather, yellow leather.
Can you say it faster?
Red leather, yellow leather.
Faster, faster, faster.

Three grey geese on the green grass grazing.
Three grey geese on the green grass grazing.

Betty Botter bought some butter,
'But,' she said, 'the butter's bitter;
If I put it in my batter,
It will make my batter bitter,
But a bit of better butter,
That would make my batter better.'

So she bought a bit of butter,
Better than her bitter butter,
And she put it in her batter,
And the batter was not bitter,
So 'twas better Betty Botter bought a bit
of better butter.

Gregory Griggs, Gregory Griggs,
Had twenty-seven different wigs.
He wore them up, he wore them down
To please the people of the town;
He wore them east, he wore them west.
But he never could tell which he liked the best!

Whether the weather be fine, or whether the weather be not,
Whether the weather be cold, or whether the weather be hot,
We'll weather the weather, whatever the weather,
Whether we like it or not.

Peter Piper picked a peck of pickled pepper,
A peck of pickled pepper Peter Piper picked.
If Peter Piper picked a peck of pickled pepper,
Where's the peck of pickled pepper Peter Piper picked?

Johnny Brown had a frown. Can you frown like Johnny Brown?
Mary Crimper had a whimper. Can you whimper like Mary Crimper?
Betty Hope had a mope. Can you mope like Betty Hope?
But Lilian Lyle had a lovely smile. Can you smile like Lilian Lyle?

Moses supposes his toeses are roses,
But Moses supposes erroneously,
For nobody's toeses are posies of roses,
As Moses supposes his toeses to be.

Fuzzy Wuzzy was a bear,
A bear was Fuzzy Wuzzy.
When Fuzzy Wuzzy lost his hair
He wasn't fuzzy, was he?

acknowledgements

I would like to thank the many friends who in so many different ways have been an invaluable help in producing this book and the music of the cassette recording, giving their time and enthusiasm with such pleasure:

Derick Last and the staff of the Ely Resource and Technology Centre, Ely, Cambs;
David, Jonathan and Robin Betts; Jasper and Jenny Kay; Don Cardy, Abigail Summers and Rachel Cardy;
Ralph Callan (Headmaster of St James Primary School, Brightlingsea, Essex) with Tobi, Clare, Jane, Caroline, Claire, Robert, Simon and Andrew;
Winifred Craig, Paul Angwin, Melanie Bees and Clive Butcher;
Angela Grunsell, Susan Eaton and Class C of Pakeman Infant School, Holloway, with their collection of playground rhymes;
Modus Operandi.

Jan Betts

The author and publisher would like to thank the following for permission to reproduce copyright material: ATV Music for 'Yellow submarine', words and music by Lennon/McCartney © 1966 Northern Songs Limited for the World; Angus & Robertson for 'The barber' by C.J. Dennis from *A Book for Kids*; 'Mine', used by permission of Atheneum Publishers from *I Feel the Same Way* by Lilian Moore. Copyright © 1967 by Lilian Moore; Adam and Charles Black for the following poems from *Speech Rhymes*: 'Ducky-Daddles', 'I saw a spider' and 'Pitter-patter' by W. Kingdon-Ward, 'Rope skipping' and 'Swing me over the water' by Ruth Large, which also appear in *Rhythm Rhymes*, 'Dandelion clocks' by J.E. Mulliner, 'Follow-my-leader', 'Going to sea', 'Marching', 'The airman', 'The dustman', 'The engine driver', 'The policeman' and 'The postman', all by Clive Sansom; Blackie and Son for 'The shiny little house' by Nancy Hayes from *A Little Book of Rhymes Old and New* by Cicely Mary Barber; British Broadcasting Corporation for 'Captain Patch' and 'Footprints', words by Tom Stanier, music by Elizabeth Bennett, from the BBC-TV programme *Watch*; 'Up, up and away' by Jim Webb from *101 Hits for Buskers* published by Wise Publications, used by kind permission of Carlin Music Corporation; *Child Education* for 'A witch wears a long tall hat' by Dave and Toni Arthur, Gerald Duckworth for 'The elephant' by Hilaire Belloc; Evans Brothers for the following: 'Mincemeat' and 'The tadpole' by Elizabeth Gould, 'Honey-Bear' by Elizabeth Lang, 'The bus' by 'Peter', 'The brown frog' by Mary Robinson, 'Snowdrops' by Mary Vivian, all from *Come Follow Me*; Aileen Fisher for her poems 'Noses', 'My puppy' and 'Upside down'; the Estate of Elizabeth Fleming for 'The window cleaner' from *The Book of a Thousand Poems* and 'In the mirror' from *Come Follow Me*, both published by Evans Brothers; the Hamlyn Publishing Group for the following: 'In the rain' by René Cloke from *A Posy of Little Verses*, 'Aeroplanes', 'Have you seen the boat leave' and 'Rocket song', all taken from *Over and Over Again* by Barbara Ireson and Christopher Rowe; William Heinemann for 'Moths and moonshine' from *Ragged Robin* and 'The sea' from *The Wandering Moon*, both by James Reeves and published by William Heinemann; David Higham Associates for the following: 'Cats' by Eleanor Farjeon from *The Children's Bells* published by Oxford University Press, 'Bedtime' and 'The tide in the river' by Eleanor Farjeon from *Silver Sand and Snow* and 'There are big waves' by Eleanor Farjeon from *Then There Were Three* both published by Michael Joseph, 'Mice and cat' by Clive Sansom from *The Golden Unicorn* published by Methuen; 'Sea shells' from *The Complete Poetical Works of Amy Lowell* © 1955 by Houghton Mifflin Company. Reprinted by permission of the publisher; Ian Humphris for 'Six little frogs' and 'Good morning, Mr Wind' from the BBC-TV programme for schools *Words and Pictures*; James Kirkup for 'The lonely scarecrow' from *Refusal to Conform* published by Oxford University Press; 'Kindness to animals' from *Tirra Lirra* by Laura E. Richards © 1935 by Laura E. Richards by permission of Little, Brown and Company; Longman Group for 'Abracadabra, wizzy-woo' and 'I'm a brave, brave mouse' by Julian Dakin from *Songs and Rhymes for the Teaching of English*; Macmillan, London and Basingstoke, for 'My motor car game' by Mona Swann from *Tippingly on the Tongue*; Methuen Children's Books for the following: 'Duck's ditty' by Kenneth Grahame from *The Wind in the Willows* © Text Copyright University Chest, Oxford, and 'Cherry stones', 'The end'. 'The engineer' and 'The wind on the hill', all by A.A. Milne from *Now We Are Six*; The Estate of Ogden Nash for 'Winter morning' from *Collected Poems* published by J.M. Dent; Oxford University Press for the following: 'I love my little donkey' by Helen Henschel from *A Third 60 Songs for Little Children*, 'Butterflies' by Frances Wood from *A Second 60 Songs for Little Children*, 'Cows' from *The Blackbird in the Lilac* by James Reeves, published by Oxford University Press (1952). Reprinted by permission of Oxford University Press; Pitman Publishing for 'Two fat gentlemen met in the lane' from *Nursery Rhymes and Finger Plays* by Boyce and Bartlett, and 'If I had plenty of money' by Paul Edmonds from *Rhymes for Children*; Russell & Volkening for 'Eggs are laid by turkeys' by Mary Ann Hoberman from *Nuts to You and Nuts to Me: An Alphabet of Poems*; Howard Sergeant for his poem 'Soft landings' from *Happy Landings* published by Evans Brothers; the Society of Authors as the literary representative of the Estate of Rose Fyleman for 'Mice' and 'Singing time' by Rose Fyleman; Stainer & Bell for the following: 'Big and strong' and 'Little Arabella Miller' by Ann Elliott from *Fingers and Thumbs*, 'We're witches of Hallowe'en' by Cynthia Raza from *Lollipop Man* reproduced by permission of Stainer & Bell Limited; World's Work for 'Sunning' from *Crickety Cricket* by James Tippett; Elizabeth Bennett for the music of 'I'm a brave, brave mouse'.

Cassette: Angus & Robertson for 'The barber' by C.J. Dennis from *A Book for Kids*; Adam and Charles Black for 'Swing me over the water' by Ruth Large from *Rhythm Rhymes*; Blackie and Son for 'The shiny little house' by Nancy Hayes from *A Little Book of Rhymes Old and New* by Cicely Mary Barber; British Broadcasting Corporation for 'Captain Patch' and 'Footprints', words by Tom Stanier, music by Elizabeth Bennett from the BBC-TV programme *Watch*; 'Up, up and away' by Jim Webb from *101 Hits for Buskers* published by Wise Publications, used by kind permission of Carlin Music Corporation; *Child Education* for 'A witch wears a long tall hat' by Dave and Toni Arthur; Evans Brothers for the following: 'The bus' by 'Peter', 'The brown frog' by Mary Robinson and 'Snowdrops' by Mary Vivian, all from *Come Follow Me*; Aileen Fisher for her poems 'Noses', 'My puppy' and 'Upside down'; 'Sea shell' from *The Complete Poetical Works of Amy Lowell* © 1955 by Houghton Mifflin Company. Reprinted by permission of the publisher; Ian Humphris for 'Six little frogs' and 'Good morning, Mr Wind' from the BBC-TV programme for schools *Words and Pictures*; Longman Group for 'I'm a brave, brave mouse' by Julian Dakin from *Songs and Rhymes for the Teaching of English*; Oxford University Press for 'Cows' from *The Blackbird in the Lilac* by James Reeves, published by Oxford University Press (1952). Reprinted by permission of Oxford University Press; Howard Sergeant for his poem 'Soft Landings' from *Happy Landings* published by Evans Brothers; The Society of Authors as the literary representative of the Estate of Rose Fyleman for 'Mice' by Rose Fyleman; Spokesmen for 'Duck's ditty' by Kenneth Grahame from *The Wind in the Willows*; Elizabeth Bennett for the music of 'I'm a brave, brave mouse'.

Every effort has been made to trace owners of copyright material, but in some cases this has not proved possible. The publisher would be glad to hear from any further copyright owners of material reproduced in **Knock at the door**.

index of first lines

Other song books from Ward Lock Educational

The Funny Family
Alison McMorland
An entertaining selection of 80 singing games, nursery rhymes and folk songs, many of which are previously unpublished, which will provide invaluable source material for playgroup leaders and primary school teachers. Alison McMorland has collected these items through her experience as a folk singer and collector of children's games.

Hokey Pokey
Alison McMorland
A further selection of songs, rhymes and games for children, collected by Alison McMorland.
Publication Autumn 1981

Folk Carols and Nursery Rhymes for Young Children
Barbara Cass-Beggs
A bright, international selection of carols and nursery rhymes chosen and arranged by Barbara Cass-Beggs. It contains many traditional Christmas carols as well as some for other festivals from several countries. A brief note on the origin of each carol and suggestions for accompanying dance movements are included, together with a short history of carols.
Publication Autumn 1980

Music titles from Ward Lock Educational

Musical Starting Points in the Classroom
Jean Gilbert
This book outlines a number of starting points in musical activities that can help the class teacher with no specialist music training to integrate the subject into the daily timetable. The singing games, finger plays and songs in the book encourage movement and dance and, ultimately, physical and emotional development. The concentration that is encouraged by these pleasurable activities will undoubtedly benefit the child's all-round learning ability.
Publication Spring 1981

Music in Action
Christine Kirk
A song book and accompanying set of chimebar/recorder charts are incorporated in this title, which is aimed at the non-specialist primary teacher. The song book contains 20 songs – nursery rhymes, folk, modern, plus some Christmas songs – each with a piano/guitar score and words. Accompanying each song are two pupil charts – one for chimebars and one for recorder – designed for use with small groups.
Publication Spring 1981